THE
REVOLUTION

Dan Luca is an expert coach, trainer and motivational speaker specializing in productivity and work–life balance for entrepreneurs and everyone who strives for a better way of life. He helps people create a lifestyle that balances family, health, hobbies, spirituality and business, so they can live their best life possible. He has created two online programmes, the 5 AM Productivity Coaching for entrepreneurs and the 5 AM Online Club for more than 1,000 early risers. Dan publishes strategies and systems that he has tested on more than thousands of his own coaching clients. Because of this extensive hands-on experience, he can vouch for his methods without blinking an eye.

The author is based in Romania. His other books include *The Dream Life Blueprint: Design and Live Your Crazy-Happy Life* and *Productivity SuperHero: Become the Most Organised and Disciplined Person You Know in 30 Days or Less* which are Kindle editions.

THE 5 A.M. REVOLUTION

Why High Achievers Wake Up Early and How You Can Do It Too

Dan Luca

RUPA

Published by
Rupa Publications India Pvt. Ltd 2017
7/16, Ansari Road, Daryaganj
New Delhi 110002

Sales centres:
Allahabad Bengaluru Chennai
Hyderabad Jaipur Kathmandu
Kolkata Mumbai

ISBN: 978-81-291-4765-3

Thirteenth impression 2020

15 14 13

Printed at Yash Printographics, Noida

Contents

Introduction

Hi!

My name is Dan Luca and I am going to guide you through this potentially life-changing journey.

I am an entrepreneur, a productivity expert, a work–life balance coach and a super-dad. For as long as I can remember, I've tried to get the most out of my life, my time and my effort. I went to great lengths, over a period of more than 18 years, to achieve the level of energy, clarity and confidence that I enjoy today.

I'll share my personal story in the next part, but before that let me tell you something.

First of all, congratulations for having the courage to make the first step in altering things towards a more fulfilling life and investing the time, energy and money to make it happen.

Secondly, I'll make sure that your journey through this course is gentle but steady as well as show you all the pieces and the ways to implement them so that this puzzle fits nicely together in the end.

Thirdly, all the things that are in this book (or course) are science based, client tested and time proven so that you get all the advantages of our research, but without the hassle of testing. Thousands of my clients are living proof that once you experience this change, you won't ever consider going back.

This programme is made up of four main parts and a bonus section. At each stage of the course, you will get all the necessary tools, templates and resources so that you can fully implement every bit of information.

The first part is about time-tested conditions and strategies you can use to achieve your best sleep possible. We'll cover all the aspects, starting with the bedroom and continuing with the evening routine, as well as techniques to make you fall asleep easier. All these and more will be duly covered.

The second part is about the morning ritual. This 10-step ritual came into existence after more than six years of fierce testing, trial and error, not to mention many 'a-ha' moments that more than a thousand clients of mine and I have experienced. You will get all the ins and outs regarding why you need to be high on energy, clarity and confidence from the first hour in the morning.

The third part is about waking up at 5 a.m. I'll give you 50 reasons to do just that. I'll teach you how to find a wake-up partner. I will also give you concrete steps to work on during the day so that you wake up more easily in the morning. All this and other fascinating stuff awaits you.

The fourth part is the 8-Week System that will take you from where you are and get you to a superhero schedule that includes all the strategies from the first three parts.

I won't talk about the bonus section now; I'll let you discover it on your own.

Now, in order to get the most out of this course and really make a change in your life, please follow these guidelines:

1. Before committing to changing any aspect of your life, please make sure that you study the entire course
2. After you have studied the three modules on Getting the Best Sleep, Practising the Morning Ritual and Waking up at 5 a.m., go straight to the 8-Week System and start implementing the actual schedule
3. Before starting the 8-Week System, make sure all of the external conditions are met:

    - The bedroom conditions

- The evening routine conditions
- The breakfast ingredients

You will get amazing results if you stick to the guidelines presented here. Otherwise, while you will still make significant changes, you'll not get the most out of this programme.

Now let me tell you how I came about creating this programme and why I am so passionate about these things.

Disclosure: I'm not getting any commission from introducing you to the devices or any other tools discussed in this programme.

My Story:
The Source of My Passion

For as long as I can remember, I have enjoyed helping people fulfil their potential and not leave all the goodness inside themselves to go to waste. In high school, I was the go-to person for little personal dramas. I always had a kind word and a strategy for my teenage friends. So, you could say that I was already a natural coach back then.

At the same time, I was passionate about flows, processes and all kinds of improvements that brought about greater efficiency. It was natural that I would go on and do a business management course at the university.

Back then, way before knowing what I wanted to do with my life, I made a promise to myself that if the management part would become my work, the people development part would remain a hobby.

For about 10 years this deal that I had struck with myself worked out pretty well and I explored a variety of positions, from being a Senior Buyer at a tech company to being a Financial Auditor in a Big 4 Auditing Company, to being a Project Manager at a Training Company, while at the same time keeping in touch with lots of different and interesting endeavours.

During that period, I witnessed and lived first-hand the 18-hour working days, a seven-days-a-week work schedule, as well as months on end of work without rest and recovery even for a single day. So, I know very well what excess looks like. I know very well how it feels to lose all your friends due to an extremely tough workload. I know how it feels to wake up in the middle of the night simply because the figures don't balance on the spreadsheet.

This was one of the most important triggers that led me into the productivity field, but without the excesses and the imbalances. I knew great things could be achieved without sacrificing health, relationships or selling one's soul.

After some extensive soul-searching, I realized that personal productivity could bring together my two lifetime passions: personal development and systems improvement.

It was once famously said that, the two most important days in your life are the day you are born, and the day you figure out why. So, every day I cherish the moment when I realized what my life is about.

I had great mentors in my life, but my dad is my hero without a shadow of doubt. And, while he was still alive, my grandfather was also a great role model.

My grandfather was a milkman and he used to get up at 4.30 a.m. to collect milk from the surrounding villages. So, he was an early riser.

On the other hand, my father was a design engineer but he worked the early shift and he would wake up at 5 a.m. so as to be at the factory by 6.30 a.m. So, he too was an early riser.

You might say that I have it in my genes, but actually it's not true, because they both HAD to wake up early to go to work and provide for their families. It was not by choice.

On the contrary, when I decided to wake up at 5 a.m. in October 2009, I didn't know anyone (personally) who had chosen to wake up early without being required to. My inspiration was Robin Sharma and his idea of the 5 a.m. Club. I had to hear and ponder over this idea of waking up early at least seven to eight times in a period of about four to five years before actually putting it into practice.

So, while it wasn't easy, I had a feeling that this shift in my lifestyle would start a domino effect that would change my life forever.

The timing of my decision was interesting too: we had just had our first son and I was working from home in the room next to where my wife and baby were. Needless to say, being so close (and presumably available), I was constantly asked to help with small stuff. My work was a mess as a result.

I then realized that the only chance I had to get any work done was to wake up earlier and work really hard before 8 a.m. when my wife and son would wake up and derail me from doing my work.

So, I started waking up at 5 a.m. and finishing more than 50 per cent of my daily schedule before 8 a.m.

I often say that 'If you don't have a choice…it's easy!'

Of course, in the initial stages of my early rising, while the baby was still small and I continued to work in that room, I was using the morning time purely for work. But, once I moved my work out of the house and started to study this way of living in more depth, I realized that this time could be better spent.

I discovered the fact that almost all great leaders in a wide range of fields wake up early in the morning. From Richard Branson to Tim Cook to Howard Schultz to Oprah Winfrey to Michael Phelps and Serena Williams, they all are early risers, mostly waking up before 6 a.m.

So, I asked myself, why? Why do all these great leaders wake up so early and not slumber in bed? They don't need to work in the morning to provide for their families.

The answer is because they want to be those people who set things in motion. They want to be proactive. They want to initiate things and make things happen. If you are asleep when your team is already up, you will be playing catch-up all day long. You will be on defence, not offence.

Yes, they wake up early every day because they all are very competitive, but this is only half the story.

A singer, before getting up on stage, warms up. An athlete, before starting a race, warms up. Any top professional, before performing in his field, warms up. The sole purpose for this is to be in peak condition. This happens when you hold yourself accountable to a very high standard. Consequently, high-performing standards deliver high-quality results.

In business, unfortunately, a lot of people are way too frequently off their best game due to a lack of proper preparation. They tend to warm up hours after the working day has started, and they eventually get into an okay state.

The alternative is to wake up earlier and put yourself in the best shape possible before starting your day. It's about making yourself strong first thing in the morning, before going out into the world. Be at your A level from the first hour of the day.

This is what I have been doing every morning for the last nine years and my life is light years ahead of what it used to be. I also started doing this same process with my clients. My productivity exploded and the productivity of my clients increased exponentially as well.

Next, I will teach you the three cornerstones for great health, incredible business results and amazing relationships.

These three things are:

- Getting the Best Sleep
- Practising the Morning Ritual
- Waking up at 5 a.m.

Talk to you soon in the first chapter.

CHAPTER ONE

GETTING THE BEST SLEEP

A. THE PERFECT BEDROOM FOR A GOODNIGHT'S SLEEP

Room design for better sleep

Imagine your bedroom as a sanctuary. When you walk in—or simply think about your bedroom—it should make you feel relaxed and peaceful. Taking care of your sleeping environment and putting thought into how it looks and feels is important, and could help you welcome more restful nights.

Start by decluttering your room and creating a clean and relatively ordered space. Arrange your furniture in a way that feels natural and visually pleasing to you. Keep computers and TVs out, so that you come to know your bedroom as a haven for sleep, free of distractions.

Choose wall colours that elicit warmth and calm. Pick colours, artwork and blankets that are soothing to you.

Also, take care of the following elements which will improve your sleep:

- Having complete darkness in your bedroom
- Eliminating all noises
- Having the optimal temperature, so that you don't feel cold or sweat during the night

Darkness

The modern bedroom is full of lights, from glowing computer monitors and clock radios to any number of blinking and glimmering electronic devices like smartphones. The trouble is chronic exposure to light at night leads to a host of health problems.

Darkness is needed for a good night's sleep. And the more the darkness the better it is. If you are having trouble sleeping and your bedroom is not totally dark when you try to sleep, you should take steps to eliminate or, at least, reduce the light.

Sleeping in complete darkness is important in getting a good night's sleep because darkness increases the production of melatonin. Melatonin is a hormone produced by the pineal gland in the brain and controls the body's sleep cycle. Melatonin is believed to cause a person to fall asleep faster and sleep better.

Research has shown that when you're exposed to light at night, even if it's brief, your leptin level decreases, which makes you hungry in the middle of the night—a phenomenon that wouldn't have been very convenient for our ancestral hunter-gatherers.

Gene expression is also affected by your internal clock, as is cellular growth and repair, and hormone production. Exposing yourself to light at night leads to the disruption of all of these processes, setting the stage for diseases like obesity, diabetes, cancer and even depression.

To achieve complete darkness, use a sleep mask. The first time I saw someone wearing a sleep mask on an airplane, I found it a bit odd. However, I changed my perception and, now, I believe that these people are brilliant. It's so difficult to create a completely dark sleep environment when you're travelling or when you want a power nap at the office and it's hard to believe the solution to this problem is so easy. Search amazon.com for Bucky Eye Mask. It has a 4.2-star rating.

Noises

While you sleep, your brain continues to register and

process sounds at a basic level. Noise can disturb your slumber—causing you to wake, move, shift between stages of sleep or experience a change in heart rate and blood pressure—so briefly that you don't remember anything the next morning. Whether sounds disturb your sleep depends on factors such as the stage of sleep you're in, the time of night and even your feelings about the sounds themselves.

Noises are more likely to wake you from a light sleep than from a deep sleep, and tend to be more disruptive in the second half of the night.

Not only can 'noise pollution' steal your slumber and make you feel drowsy the next day, there is evidence that sounds such as those from constant, loud urban traffic may have a negative effect on health.

According to research published in *Environmental Health Perspectives*, long-term exposure to traffic noise may account for approximately 3 per cent of coronary heart disease deaths (or about 2,10,000 deaths) in Europe each year. Scientists concluded that the percentage of affected people is similar in America and Asia. But, how exactly does noise harm your heart?

One of the key ways is by elevating stress hormones such as cortisol, adrenaline and noradrenaline, which, over time, can lead to high blood pressure, stroke and heart failure.

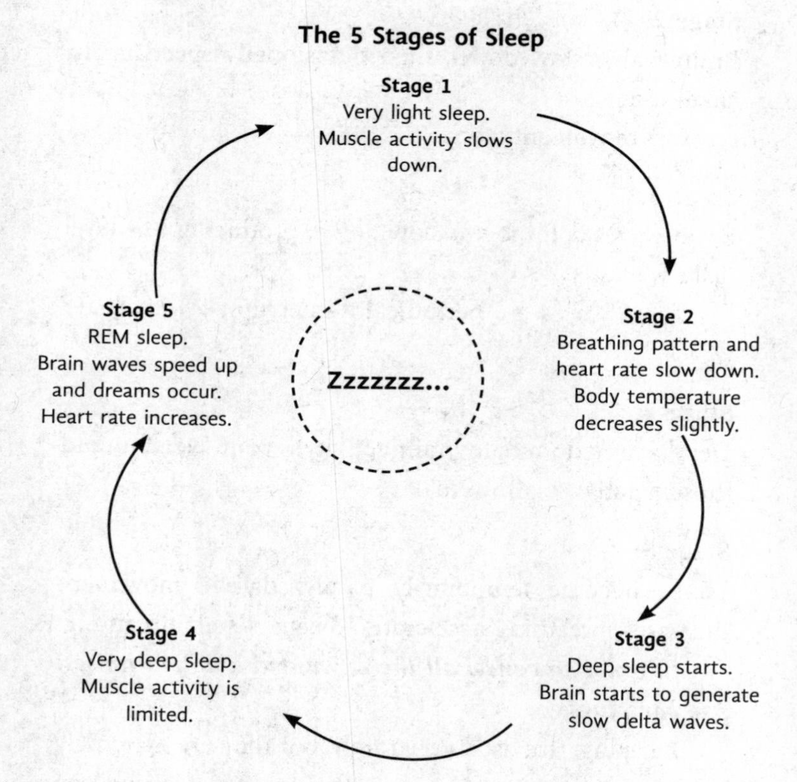

STAGES OF SLEEP

Stage 1:

Muscles begin to relax.

A person drifting in and out of sleep and can be easily awakened.

Stage 2:
Brain waves slow down, then occasionally speed up in small bursts.

Eye movement stops.

Stage 3:
Brain waves continue to slow down, producing low level delta waves.

These waves are periodically interrupted with faster waves.

Stage 4:
Delta waves dominate brain activity; eye movement and muscle activity is minimal.

Stage 5:
Limbs become temporarily paralyzed; eye movement increases, breathing accelerates. Sleepers start dreaming.

In order to cancel all the unwanted ambient noises, use ear plugs.

Ear plugs are used very rarely, but they are extremely useful if you want to increase the quality of your sleep both at home as well as in other spaces where sleeping would be impossible. You put the ear plugs in, pull your sleep mask over your eyes, and this is how you turn any waiting period into a refreshing and productive use of your time. You can search Amazon for Hearos Ear Plugs. It has a rating of above 4 stars.

Optimal Temperature

The ideal sleeping temperature that is recommended by every study I have found ranges from 60 to 68 degrees F (or 16 to 20 degrees Celsius), but most studies recommend setting your thermostat to about 65 degrees F (18.5 degrees C), and the American Academy of Sleep Medicine agrees to this, too.

Before you go to sleep, your body's internal temperature drops, which 'promotes deep continuous sleep'. Setting your thermostat to around 65 degrees F (18.5 degrees C) will help your body get to that temperature faster, which will let you fall asleep faster, and sleep better. This is why exercising or eating a large meal close to bedtime disrupts your sleep: both activities raise your body's core temperature.

Keep in mind that everyone's ideal sleeping temperature is different, and what's comfortable for you might not be comfortable for your partner. The key is to keep your bedroom at a 'thermally neutral' temperature. According to scientists, 'thermally neutral means that our body doesn't have to do anything to create heat (shiver) or shed heat (sweat) to compensate for being too cold or too warm.'

As a general idea, the American Academy of Sleep Medicine suggests: think of the bedroom as a cave; it should be cool, quiet and dark.

The easiest way to keep in check all the bedroom variables: CubeSensors (Koto).

Of course you can monitor a lot of the existing conditions in your bedroom by yourself, but if you have a busy family life with a spouse, children and maybe even pets, you know things can get crazy.

So, while searching for an intelligent way to keep things within the optimum standards, I came across CubeSensors (Koto).

CubeSensors (Koto) is a family of smart sensors that monitor your indoor environment and let you know when you can make simple improvements that will keep your home and family healthy. They are revolutionary because they have seven different sensors measuring air quality, temperature, humidity, noise, light, weather pressure and movement (vibrations).

You can get two, four or six CubeSensors (Koto) and place them in different rooms with different ambient features. Your office is different from your bedroom and the kids' room.

A CubeSensor (Koto) can tell you when the temperature in your home is off, costing you money, or alert you that your office is too dark to be working without lights being on as the sun starts to go down. Plus, it tells you about indoor pollution, ensuring that the air you breathe in your home is fresh and clean.

Feedback is given based on what you want to do in that room, either with a shake prompted glowing light, or in more detail via a Web app.

If you've assigned one of the CubeSensors (Koto) to sleep, you can also pair it with a sleep-tracking Fitbit or Jawbone device. This lets you see the data from the CubeSensors (Koto) along with that from the fitness tracker simultaneously, with the idea being that you can see if the room temperature, humidity or light coming in through the window is causing periods of disrupted sleep. Not only will you know how many times you woke up, but also the reasons.

Google search words: 'CubeSensors' and 'Koto' for more information.

Next, we'll talk about the daytime habits that can increase the quality of your sleep. If you ignore them, or even worse, do the opposite, you might experience low quality of sleep, which will have a serious impact on your health and performance. Make sure you do the next five things properly and avoid the four that impair your sleep considerably.

B. DAYTIME HABITS FOR A BETTER SLEEP

Get 30 minutes of sunlight

Light sends your brain the signal that it's time to wake up. This aspect is most likely obvious for everybody who's turned on the light in the middle of the night and then had problems getting back to sleep.

What's not so obvious, however, is the fact that exposing yourself to natural light at other times, especially during the first hours of the morning, can actually help you sleep better at night.

Natural light is a factor that helps regulate your biological clock, keeping it on the right track. This 'internal clock' is located in the brain and it's not so different from a regular hand watch.

The moment of exposure is crucial. Your body's clock is the most receptive towards sunlight in the morning, between 6 a.m. and 8.30 a.m. Then, it practically resets your internal clock, which regulates the sleep–wake cycle.

Drink enough water

Amazingly, an estimated 75 per cent of Americans are chronically dehydrated! Simply eating water-rich foods and drinking more water could be one of the healthiest changes you can make to bring about better sleep and to improve your health.

Water makes up about 60 per cent of your body, 75 per cent is in your muscles, and **85 per cent is in your brain**. Water is essential for almost all of your bodily functions, especially the brain function. So, it shouldn't come as a surprise that being dehydrated may disrupt healthy brain function while sleeping.

For all of these functions to be optimally fulfilled, you need approximately 68 fl. oz. (or 2 litres) of good-quality water every day. This doesn't include other liquids such as sodas, soups, coffee, etc.

This means you can satisfy this daily water requirement by drinking a 9-ounce (or 260 ml) glass of water every two hours. It's important that you drink water as soon as possible after waking up and then at regular intervals throughout the day, especially in the first half of the day.

While we sleep, our body uses the water it already has, but it doesn't have the opportunity to 'refill its tank'. So, it's vital that you drink 16 fl. oz. (or 500 ml) of water right after waking up. Information about optimal water temperature and what you can put in the water to make it more beneficial for your body can be found in the later section of Morning Ritual.

I don't recommend that you drink more than 9 ounces (or 260 ml) of water an hour before bedtime because, otherwise, you'll have to go to the bathroom at night and this will negatively impact the quality of your sleep.

Exercise for 30 minutes

Another determining factor for a restful sleep is exercising during the day.

Everybody who exercises has far fewer problems with their sleep pattern But what's even more interesting is that people who are in great physical shape need less sleep!

Why?

Because their bodies regenerate much more quickly and they resort to other sources of energy besides sleep such as highly functioning muscles, flexible joints, increased pulmonary capacity and many more. Most people recharge energetically just by sleeping and, therefore, lose the opportunity to gain vital energy through physical exercise.

I will start by mentioning a few obvious benefits of exercise:

- Allows better cell oxygenation because your breathing is improved and this will help you inhale and exhale more deeply
- Improves the efficient elimination of toxins by improving the circulation of the lymphatic system
- Tones the muscles and increases your resistance to physical effort

- Optimizes your general state of health
- Stimulates the secretion of endorphins ('happiness hormones'), therefore, your mood is greatly improved
- The most powerful changes occur when those with sedentary jobs (desk jobs) start getting some physical exercise
- 'Static' workplaces predispose you to shallow breathing, insufficient brain and muscle oxygenation, compacted vertebrae, joint pains, tired eyes, accumulated tension in the shoulder blades, neck stiffness, and much more
- If you're not used to following a daily routine, I suggest that you experiment with something little less aggressive, something you can do with a minimum of effort and that will combat the issues mentioned above
- Start with five minutes of walking around your building complex. Breathe, relax, clear your mind and unclench your muscles
- After three days, increase the duration to 10 minutes
- After another three days, increase the duration to 15 minutes
- At some point, you'll actually want to start running at a slow pace…don't fight it!

- After more time has passed, you'll start running faster and longer...let your body dictate the rhythm
- Why do I believe this to be the best way to start exercising?
- Because after you get dressed and put on your sneakers, immediately after walking out the door, you're at 'your gym' or at the 'race track'. You shorten the length of time it takes to get started and you eliminate any major obstacles that might hold you back
- So, take it literally...step by step...but BE CAREFUL!
- Discipline yourself to not do less than what you set out to do, but also to not do more than that!
- This aspect is very important! If your goal is to exercise for 10 minutes, don't exercise for 20 minutes...you'll do that when you get to the appropriate stage. Measure your effort so you avoid stimulating self-sabotage
- The best time to go for a walk and then for a jog is in the morning. However, do not implement this habit before practicing the Morning Routine. In the last part of the course, the 8-Week System, I'll tell you exactly when you should incorporate walking and then running during your morning activities

The power nap

In 1975, Dr Roger Broughton from the University of Ottawa argued that afternoon naps are a natural part of the human sleep cycle.

This seemed radical to those who saw naps as indicating laziness or being specific to some tropical societies. After a period of ignoring napping, scientists started to study it in 1986.

Dr Broughton discovered that, even after a full night's rest, people still have a strong tendency to fall asleep early in the afternoon.

We tend to ignore this issue for practical reasons and because of our work schedule. Therefore, it would be good to regulate our wakefulness at the same time every day.

The second wave of fatigue hits approximately eight hours after waking up in the morning. Therefore, if you are getting up between 5 a.m. and 7 a.m., you'll probably start feeling tired again during the afternoon, between 1.30 p.m. and 3 p.m.

A short nap of about 10-20 minutes can satisfy the desire for sleep and allows you to wake up feeling more alert and rested.

A research, published in 2007, by Harvard's School of Public Health in the US along with the University of Athens Medical School was conducted over a period of six years on a batch of 24,000 men and women.

The results of this study showed that a short nap, in the early afternoon, can decrease the risk of cardiovascular diseases by 34 per cent.

NASA conducted studies on astronauts and pilots to determine the best sleep patterns for the maintenance of maximum performance.

They discovered that a short nap can improve performance by 34 per cent and vigilance by 54 per cent.

Some people swear that dozing off makes them feel even sleepier. However, a short nap of less than 20 minutes should perk almost anybody up.

'Ten to twenty minutes are enough to take advantage of the benefits of a nap such as increased vigilance, improved performance, and an overall better mood', the researchers from Brock University in Ontario explain.

Here's why:

While we are asleep, our brain produces different types of waves that correspond to the depth level of our sleep. After approximately 20 minutes, the sleepy brain can enter a phase called slow-wave sleep, the most profound sleeping phase.

This is why, if you doze off too much, you can feel light-headed and disoriented when you wake up, instead of feeling refreshed.

If you have the possibility of turning your afternoon nap into a daily habit, get comfortable with using something you associate with sleep (a lavender-scented pillow, an eye mask, ear plugs, etc.) to fall asleep faster.

Also, choose a rocking chair or a couch instead of a bed to reduce the temptation of sleeping too much.

It's very important not to exceed 30 minutes of sleep in the afternoon and to make sure you nap before or up until 3 p.m. Otherwise, you will disrupt your circadian cycle and it will be extremely difficult for you to go to bed in the evening at the hour that you want.

As a side note, our internal circadian cycle regulates the timing of periods of sleepiness and wakefulness throughout the day. It's our internal clock that keeps us in sync with our natural rhythm of being.

If you want to sleep the 'exact' optimum amount of time every afternoon, follow these steps:

- Grab a set of keys or a small metallic object
- Sit or lie down in a comfortable position but extend the hand that's holding the metallic object outwards, away from the bed or armchair so that after you fall asleep, the keys or that object, will fall to the ground on a hard surface and produce a loud noise
- Right when your hand relaxes, you enter the deep sleep phase and this is the best time to wake up before your body starts producing analgesics for the fourth stage of deep sleep

To return to your usual rhythm quickly, after taking a power nap, add the following three steps to your routine:

- Drink a cup of coffee right before you take the nap—your body needs approximately 20 minutes to absorb and assimilate caffeine, thus helping you wake up exactly after 20 minutes
- Drink a glass of water at room temperature right after waking up to get fluid into your blood and help it oxygenate better
- Move around, do some stretching exercises after waking up to restart your metabolism and help your body produce more energy

Dinner

Your evening meal represents an essential source of energy that can make a huge difference when it comes to the quality of your sleep—whether it's an agitated or laboured one or a type of sleep that allows all of your bodily functions to take place under optimal conditions.

There are a great number of myths regarding the best time to have dinner and what it should consist of.

The basic principle is that some foods stimulate the brain while others soothe it and get it ready for sleep. Therefore, you should eat more foods from the second category and less from the first.

The most important element that your brain needs so as to enjoy adequate sleep is a substance called tryptophan.

It's the raw material that your body uses to produce serotonin and melatonin—two substances that induce sleep. Hence, you should avoid meals rich in protein—which stimulate the brain—before going to bed.

For a peaceful and restful sleep you should also avoid:

- Hearty meals less than four hours before going to bed (e.g. steak and potatoes or other dense nutritional dishes)
- Fatty or spicy foods
- Tomatoes, potatoes and onions

Eat foods that induce relaxation and sleepiness such as:

- Raw almonds (they contain tryptophan and magnesium), walnuts (and other nuts) and pumpkin seeds
- Oatmeal (contains melatonin and regulates the sleep process)
- Bananas (they are rich in magnesium and melatonin)
- Mushrooms (they are rich in easily assimilable proteins and give a quick filler effect)
- Avocados, grapefruit and papayas (they are rich in magnesium)

But, by far, the best investment you can make when it comes to getting a good night's sleep—according to nutrition expert Michael Greger, MD[1]—is eating two kiwis an hour before bedtime. Kiwi is a fruit rich in antioxidants, which reduce oxidative stress, and it also contains serotonin and folate.

What to avoid during the day and evening

- **No caffeine after 3 p.m.**—Many people have a very low tolerance for coffee. It's important to observe and notice any type of patterns you might have regarding coffee. The effects of coffee can last up to six hours, so if you want to go to sleep at 10 p.m. make sure you don't drink any coffee past 3 p.m.
- **No alcohol after 3 p.m.**—Having an evening drink offers you a few benefits, but lots of negative ones as well. You're more likely to fall asleep faster after a drink. And you're even going to get about half a night of decent sleep, but afterwards you're more likely to wake up and sleep less deeply. It will interrupt your circadian cycle and will block your rapid eye movement sleep, which is the most restorative type of sleep.

---

[1]https://drgreger.org/pages/about-us

You will have a shallow sleep and wake up sooner without feeling rested.

Hours later, when your body has mostly assimilated the alcohol, your sleep becomes fragmented, and prone to frequent awakenings (often to hit the bathroom). You may also struggle with snoring, night sweats, nightmares, headaches and insomnia.

If, however, you find yourself, once in a while, in a social setting and you're drinking, make sure you follow the 1-for-1 rule. Drink one glass of water for every glass of alcohol to help prevent dehydration. And down a few extra glasses of water the next morning, too.

- **No smoking after 7 p.m.**—People who smoke a few hours before bedtime struggle to fall asleep because nicotine disrupts their natural sleep–wake cycle, and withdrawal symptoms set in before the morning alarm clock goes off, often leaving them feeling even more restless and agitated.
- **No screen time after 8 p.m.**—Smartphones, TV, tablets and computers radiate a blue light, which prevents the release of melatonin in your body. Melatonin, a hormone that helps you fall asleep, should be released at the right time so that you fall asleep quickly each night.

You have two options for stopping the blue light from keeping you up at night. The first, and perhaps the better option, is to set a specific time to turn off all blue light devices, generally about two to three hours before retiring to bed. You should pick a time and follow it with consistency so that it becomes a natural part of the routine. Your mind will relax, release melatonin and be much better prepared to fall asleep when you want to.

Another option, though less convenient, is to wear blue-blocking sunglasses, which can be useful if you absolutely must look at any of these screens before getting some shut-eye. But all in all, simply limiting your exposure to blue light altogether before bed is probably the better idea.

But, if you *really* have to watch or read something from your devices, in order to block the blue light and avoid the impact on your sleep, install the app called *f.lux* on that device. This will diminish your exposure to blue light and keep the melatonin to a normal level up to the point when you finally go to bed.

Next, we'll talk about the evening routine, and about what makes a great go-to-bed schedule. It might look simple or straightforward, but it is not. I guarantee that if you follow these steps, you'll have the most pleasant and easy transition from being awake to having a great night's sleep. See you then.

C. EVENING ROUTINE

The evening routine alarm

One of the most frequent objections I usually receive is that it's easy to lose track of time in the evening. You play with your kids, surf the Web, watch your favourite TV show, read an interesting book…and it's already past your optimal bedtime.

From my experience, I can tell you that this is a legitimate challenge that could knock you off of your ideal schedule.

The solution I have found is to set an alarm clock for going to bed.

This works differently than the alarm clock I use for waking up because I don't set the alarm to ring at the exact time that I'm supposed to close my eyes, rather I set the alarm 30 minutes earlier so that I have enough time to finish what I have started.

You can now use apps like Bedtime that comes pre-installed on your iPhone or SleepyTime on your Android phone.

This 'go-to-bed' alarm is an early, friendly warning that I use to remind myself that I have no choice but to be ready for bed in 30 minutes (tops!).

I have reached a point where I can use this habit with my kids as well and it works really well because they love predictability and the fact that I don't tell them to 'go to bed NOW'.

Just like adults, children can self-manage much better when things are predictable and you set boundaries neither of you will be tempted to negotiate later.

Concretely, set your alarm clock for 9.30 p.m. (if you want to be in bed by 10 p.m.) and notice how your chances of respecting your bedtime increase from 10-20 per cent to 90-95 per cent!

To make the 30-minute process before going to bed simple and predictable, I suggest you use three elements—a visual element, an auditory element and a kinaesthetic element. You can choose to use just the one that you find the most relevant or you can combine them in any way you like.

The visual element: Right after your 'go-to-bed' alarm goes off, go into the bedroom and turn on your bedside lamp. Turn off any other light that was already on in that room.

The auditory element: Listen to a music CD that you like and increase the volume a bit so that you can hear the music even when you leave the bedroom to finish activities you started in other rooms.

The kinaesthetic element: Right after you turn on your bedside lamp and turn up the music in your bedroom, place a rubber band on the wrist of your dominant hand. This is useful especially for the activities you have to do outside the bedroom during those 30 minutes. You might not see the light from the bedside lamp or hear the music coming from the bedroom, but you'll quickly notice the rubber band on your wrist.

Step 1. Review of the day—10 minutes

Begin the 30 minutes of your bedtime routine with a review of the day. I recommend you do this in the bedroom to benefit from the three helpful elements: the bedside lamp, the music and the rubber band.

The daily review is important because your mind relaxes when you give it the opportunity to close out the experience of the current day, evaluate what worked and what didn't and capitalize on what you learned.

This way you'll be able to feel comfortable because you have 'completed' the current day and also feel that you've got things under control, even if you didn't manage to finish everything you set out to do that day and had to reschedule some activities for the next day.

Concretely, it's enough to spend 10 minutes asking yourself the questions below. Don't let yourself be tricked by the fact that it's only 10 minutes.

This time will have a very important influence on your future success because it ensures you evolve and develop 1 per cent each day.

The questions are the following:

- What worked today? (at least five examples)
- What didn't work today?
- What have I learned today? (at least three examples)
- What will I do differently tomorrow?
- What am I grateful for today? (at least three examples)

I do my 'Review for the Day' while drinking my favourite tea.

I use my cup of tea as a way to sit down and really let myself land the plane. It's a great way to settle in the energy of the evening and really let the body know that I'm getting ready to sleep.

Best choices of tea include jasmine, caraway, chamomile or anise, as they have tryptophan.

A word of caution: drink the tea without lemon, as the smell of it (or other citrus fruits) can boost mental stimulation and increase energy levels, which may then hamper your sleep.

Step 2. Clothes for tomorrow—Five minutes

While in the bedroom—in the dressing, to be more precise—choose and organize your clothes for the next day. This way, you'll avoid the drama that occurs among most families every morning with questions like 'where are my socks?', 'where's my scarf?', 'who took my belt?'... so on and so forth.

For example, setting out all of your gym clothes and gear can be the first step in the right direction to motivate you to carry out your planned workout, which is a good part to have in a morning routine.

No matter what you have to do the next morning, having already taken this one step related to your morning routine is sure to save you time and mental energy that can be applied to more productive activities.

Step 3. Bathroom necessities—Five minutes

I think this is straightforward, no need to elaborate here.

Step 4. Brush teeth and floss—Five minutes

This one should also be pretty straightforward. Just a word of caution: studies have shown that toothpaste together with peppermint tend to stimulate the brain and make it feel more awake.

Step 5. Prayer or meditation—Five minutes

This one is subject to personal preference. I can give you several options and you can choose the one that serves you best:

A) Prayer

The best prayer I know (regardless of personal faith) is the one that entails offering thanks to all the good things that have happened during the day. So it's a prayer of gratitude.

Like attracts like, so if you are thankful and acknowledging what is good in your life, you will have more. Find 10 to 20 things to be grateful for and you will transform any existing anxiety into serotonin, which will actually give you a better night's sleep.

B) Meditation

If you prefer something other than prayer, you can choose from the following alternatives:

- **The Hawaiian meditation**—which is described in the Morning Ritual
- **A free content meditation**—which, simply put, is just sitting in silence with your eyes closed and acknowledging your breath. Just a straightforward way to calm down, clear you mind and relax your body
- **Headspace app**—is a great way to start meditating if you are relatively new to it. Besides all the meditations for the other moments of the day and various purposes, it also has a meditation for

better sleep at night. It's very good and I highly recommend it

Now, with all these activities, 30 minutes have passed since the alarm went off and you are now ready to call it a day.

All the previous five steps allowed your body and mind to wind down and settle into a very relaxed mood that is optimal for a great sleep. Here's a recap:

- You started by closing all the loops and integrating the relevant aspects of the day
- You went on to drink a nice warm tea with ingredients that infused your body with tryptophan
- You continued with the preparation of the next day's clothes
- You also took a toilet break
- Immediately followed by the brushing and flossing of the teeth
- Right before getting into the bed, you had a five-minute session of prayer or meditation

All I can tell you right now is goodnight and have a great sleep!

If you have a history of unsatisfactory sleep, make sure you learn all the great techniques and strategies that I teach in the next module.

D. TECHNIQUES TO FALL ASLEEP

Self-relaxation

'There is no need to go to India or anywhere else to find peace. You will find that deep place of silence right in your room, your garden or even your bathtub.'

—Elisabeth Kübler-Ross

I'll offer you some general guidelines after telling you what the method's principles are and how to effectively practise this exercise.

It's about using relaxation elements and self-hypnosis to achieve the best possible state before falling asleep.

If you're not very familiar with hypnosis, especially self-hypnosis, you don't have to preoccupy your mind with these notions right now because the process is simple and you're the one who will be giving yourself the beneficial suggestions.

All you have to do is lie down on your bed, on your back, with your hands and legs extended, without crossing them, and breathe regularly. The basic principle is to 'scan' your body by focusing your attention from the heels to the top of your head and gradually relax each part of your body.

It's more important that you understand the principle rather than the method. You can replace the words if you feel it's necessary to do so, but keep in mind the general spirit of the principle.

And now, regarding the process that you can go through to relax profoundly and get ready to go to sleep:

> 'I can feel my toes. I am becoming aware of the sensations I feel in my toes. My toes are more and more relaxed... I feel my heels and my ankles, I relax them even more...my feet are more and more relaxed.
>
> I now shift my attention upwards. My calves are becoming increasingly relaxed. My calves are very, very relaxed. And my knees are relaxed. They're very, very relaxed.
>
> I shift my attention to my thighs and I relax them even more. My thighs are very, very relaxed.
>
> My pelvic region is relaxing. I can feel the relaxation becoming more and more profound. My buttocks are very, very relaxed.
>
> I now shift my attention towards my abdomen and I relax it even more...and my lower back is becoming increasingly relaxed... My chest is relaxed; it's becoming more and more relaxed... I can feel my back relaxing as well. This relaxation sensation finds its way upwards to the back of my neck.
>
> My fingers are completely relaxed. My wrists and forearms are very, very relaxed and my attention shifts upwards towards my elbows and my arms that are very, very relaxed.

And now I profoundly relax my shoulders and shift my attention towards my neck that is increasingly more relaxed.

I relax my jaw and jawbone more and more…I can feel my tongue relaxing in my mouth, as are the muscles of my face, my cheekbones… I relax my earlobes, the area around my eyes and my forehead; they are all becoming increasingly more relaxed.

I breathe easily and relax and revel in this state of complete relaxation.'

If you fall asleep during this process it's OK, don't worry about it. The goal here is not so much finishing the process as it is putting yourself in a state of deep relaxation.

I'll say it once again because it's essential: it's very important that you focus your attention in each moment on exactly the area that you wish to relax.

It's much simpler than it seems when you actually practise it, so good luck!

Positive affirmations and emotional freedom

Forgiveness is the fragrance that the violet sheds
on the heel that has crushed it.
—Mark Twain

Next, I would like to tell you about the easiest and most simple way of falling asleep peacefully.

Most people who have trouble sleeping or experience restless sleep have completely counterproductive bedtime habits like watching news or highly stimulating shows on TV just before bed, trying to solve the unfinished businesses from that day or going to bed feeling upset about a conversation with their spouse or their child.

What I suggest you do now is take a closer look at what you do right after getting in bed and preparing yourself to close your eyes. Do you think about good things or bad parts of the day?

I know many people who have the habit of thinking about unfinished tasks and their possible solutions. This habit predictably generates anxiety and stress.

This habit wouldn't be much of a problem if it actually worked and they would find valid solutions to the problems they're thinking about. But when you're in that semi-conscious state, your thinking is not structured and, most likely, the most frustrating thing is that if you did find a viable solution, you wouldn't be able to remember it in the morning, unless you wrote it down right then and there.

I believe the time before you go to bed should be spent differently.

To be more specific, the most beneficial way is to release any anxiety you might feel in your body and achieve a state of calm, relaxation and emotional comfort.

And, the best way to release anxiety and fall asleep and calm down is by practising an emotional release exercise immediately after your head hits the pillow.

This method is very useful for those who have a very active mind before going to bed. In essence, what you do is you repeat four affirmations that put you into a relaxed state and connect all four intelligences (physical, mental, emotional and spiritual). Tell these affirmations to yourself and you imagine taking a shower 'on the inside' and releasing any trace of discomfort and anxiety.

The four affirmations you'll repeat while feeling the corresponding emotions are:

1. I release any negative emotions or thoughts that I have gathered throughout the day
2. I am grateful for everything I have learned and I am content with everything I have accomplished today
3. I will have a restful sleep and an excellent day tomorrow
4. I'm relaxing more and more and I'm getting ready to fall asleep

Therefore, I encourage you to practise this process as soon as your head hits the pillow. This way you'll give your 'system' the opportunity to harmonize and find the

calm and relaxation that will make it easier fo
have a restful sleep.

You can repeat these affirmations in your head until you fall asleep. Try not to think about anything else and repeat these affirmations thinking about what they mean to you and what the personal significance is.

The four-step process you can do if you can't sleep (after you're in bed)

Have you ever experienced a time when you simply couldn't fall asleep even though you were very tired?

Remember the last time you had difficulties in making a payment…or the time your kid had a very important exam coming up the next day…or the time you had your annual check-up and didn't know how the results will turn up? All these instances come with a very high emotional roller coaster.

I know a lot of ways that can help you relax or resolve the issues that are keeping you from sleeping and generating a state of anxiety.

Depending on how serious the issue is, you can follow one or more steps from the process I describe below. I have tested this process for myself and my coaching clients have tried it out as well. I can't guarantee you that it will work 100 per cent of the time, but I can tell you that the success rate of this process is somewhere around 90 per cent. The other 10 per cent may need medication or specialized interventions.

What I'm actually trying to say is, why don't you take advantage of a process that has a 90 per cent success rate?

Test this process and if it doesn't work for you no matter how many times you try it, then you should address the issue by seeking out professional help. If you truly have trouble sleeping, I'm curious to know what your feedback will be after practising this process.

Let's get to work and see what the steps are:

Step 1. Paradoxical intent

The paradoxical intent is a method that's quite easy to put into practice and also inexplicably effective. All you have to do is get into bed, close your eyes and try to stay AWAKE for as long as you can.

It's very important that you keep your eyes closed and concentrate on staying awake. Thus, you should focus your attention on a single element, eliminate any other thoughts and start to gently fall asleep.

As a side note, Paradoxical Intention is a cognitive technique that consists of persuading yourself to engage in your most feared behaviour. In the context of sleep problems, this type of solution is based on the idea that the pressure to fall asleep inhibits sleep itself. Paradoxically, if you stop trying so hard to fall asleep and instead try to stay awake for as long as possible, the anxiety is expected to diminish; thus, sleep may occur more easily.

Step 2. Relax

If you have already spent 20 minutes in bed and you still haven't been able to fall asleep using the paradoxical intent, it might be necessary for you to get up and do some of the following:

- Make yourself a nice cup of jasmine tea and add honey to help your body release melatonin. This substance will induce a state of sleepiness that will help you fall asleep
- Alternatively, you can drink chamomile, anise or caraway tea
- Relax and practise visualizing your body from head to toe
- Listen to relaxing music. There are a lot of playlists of this type on YouTube. Just search using the phrase 'music for sleep'

Moreover, it's important for you to know that if you have trouble sleeping, watching TV before going to bed is not recommended—it's true that for some people the TV acts as some sort of 'sleeping pill'. However, that is not the case for most people. Furthermore, it induces low-quality sleep because of the subconscious suggestions that you receive just before going to bed. So, best is to avoid watching TV at least by two hours before going to bed.

Also, because of the noise, the TV, which you left on, might wake you up in the middle of the night, thus interrupting your sleep. At the same time, the light projected off the TV screen prevents the release of natural analgesics in your body that are necessary for falling asleep.

Step 3. Take the load off

If you're not able to fall asleep even after drinking tea, listening to relaxing music and visualizing, it might be time to let go of the things that are stressing you out.

Therefore, grab a piece of paper and ask yourself: 'What is the thing that is keeping me from falling asleep?'

After you answer the question and you unload any feelings of stress or anxiety, you'll most likely find yourself in a peaceful state, conducive for sleep.

Find as many reasons as you can to convince yourself that the pessimistic scenario you've envisioned will not come to life. Find as many elements as you can that will fill you up with strength.

Step 4. Paradoxical intent

After releasing from your system anything that was keeping you from sleeping, you can go back to bed and practise the first step. Now, you'll most certainly be ready to fall asleep.

It's very important that you avoid looking at the watch during all this time because doing so will stress you out even more.

Next, make sure to read and rate your sleep according to The Great Sleep Checklist. Print it out and use it daily to see if you are on the right track. This way, you can track any slip-ups easily. Use it and improve your sleep, starting today.

E. THE GREAT SLEEP CHECKLIST

During the day

1. Did you wake up this morning at the time you had planned to last night?
2. Did you manage to wake up immediately after the alarm clock went off?
3. On a scale of 1 to 10, how rested did you feel this morning right after getting out of bed?
4. Did you expose yourself to natural sunlight for 30 minutes between 6 a.m. and 8.30 a.m.?
5. Did you drink at least 68 fl. oz. of water during the day?
6. Did you exercise for at least 30 minutes today?

7. Did you avoid drinking coffee after lunch?

At night, before going to bed

1. Did you set out to be in bed by 10 p.m.?
2. Did you set your alarm clock 30 minutes before the hour you would like to be in bed by?
3. Did you eat at least four hours before going to bed?
4. Did you especially eat vegetables and fruits that stimulate the production of melatonin (bananas, nuts or kiwis)?
5. Did you avoid drinking alcohol, coffee, eating chocolate or smoking before going to bed?
6. Did you set your alarm clock so that you were able to sleep between seven and eight hours?
7. Do you have a pillow that helps you relieve any tension you might feel along your spine?
8. Do you have a quilt that ensures optimal thermal comfort during the night (you shouldn't be sweating nor feeling cold)?
9. Do you have comfortable pajamas?
10. Is your room quiet? If you hear any external noises you can't control, do you use ear plugs?
11. Is the room temperature between 60 degrees F and 68 degrees F?
12. Is your room dark during the night? Do you use

a face mask if it's not dark enough?

13. Did you avoid practising activities in the bedroom that stimulate your intellect for at least two hours before going to bed?
14. Did you complete your daily review to alleviate your emotions?
15. Did you organize your to-do list for the next day so that you can feel you have things under control?

CHAPTER TWO

THE MORNING RITUAL

Before I begin, please allow me to tell you something from my not-so-distant past.

I remember I used to press the snooze button at least twice each morning.

I remember I used to think that waking up early was a burden and I dreamt about the day when I could wake up at whatever hour I wanted to.

It took me more than two or three hours and two or three cups of coffee to get me going at, what I now call, my 20 per cent-effectiveness mode.

I used to work until 9 p.m. or 10 p.m., weekends too, and get mad at my wife because she didn't understand how important my work was.

Most of the time I skipped breakfast, or on my best mornings, I ate what I then called a healthy breakfast: 'eggs and bacon'.

I remember that at 4 p.m. I was exhausted and used up all my will and discipline to keep on working and I remember that I did all that without having two kids and my own business.

I was wondering, 'How the hell am I going to be able to start a business and have kids without going insane?'

After a lot of struggle, and morning cursing, I had the fortune to understand that my power was in the mornings.

So, I started waking up at 5 a.m. and had the goal of taking care of myself first!

I went through a lot of rituals and habits, and, at one time, my morning ritual lasted for more than three hours!

Over a period of time, I realized that three hours was not sustainable and, moreover, it was not something that everyone could do.

So I took all my habits and started a quest to reinvent them.

I wanted to fit all these habits into less than an hour and still get 80 per cent of the benefits.

I will take them, one by one, and detail them for you, so that you reap all the benefits from my quest that started more than nine years ago.

I will show you habits that will increase your energy

in the body, habits that will increase the clarity in your mind, habits that will increase your level of confidence and habits that will put front and center your highest motivation so that you go all the way on the projects that matter most for you.

Let's begin!

A. GRATITUDE FOR AN EXTRAORDINARY DAY

What is this?

It's a practice that sets the tone for the day. It's a fast and easy way to put yourself in a great state during the first few minutes of the day.

Why is it great?

Gratitude has the benefit of releasing the hormone oxytocin which counters any hormones that get released due to anxiety, such as cortisol (also known as the stress hormone).

So, how are you going to do this? What are you going to write about?

All you have to do is take two minutes and start writing all the things that you are grateful for.

You can use the phrase: 'I am so grateful that...'

The topics of your gratitude can include:

- Health, spouse, children, money, clients, parents, friends, knowledge and things less obvious such as…
- Hot water, food, shelter, a bed, clothes to wear, your eyesight, your ability to walk, the fact that you live in a peaceful country, that you have freedom of speech and the freedom to pursue your dreams.

The best time and place to do this

While you brush your teeth you can practise gratitude. You read and feel the things you consider to be the most important for you and your life.

It is easier to link a new habit to an existing one. And brushing the teeth is something that almost 100 per cent of the people do in the morning. Therefore, use it to add another good habit for you.

Exercise

Please take two minutes and write down on a post-it note at least five things that you are grateful for right now. After three days, you can replace the post-it note with another one containing another five items and so on and so forth.

B. HOT WATER WITH LEMON AND TURMERIC

What is this?

It's an extremely simple but very powerful habit. Drink 17 ounces (or 500 ml) of water at room temperature mixed with the juice of half a lemon and a half teaspoon of turmeric.

While you were asleep your body used up a lot of water to regulate your body temperature, repair your tissues, etc. Offer your body the opportunity to start the day in an optimum rhythm as soon as you wake up.

Why is it great?

- It improves your digestion
- It helps your liver release bile, a digestive enzyme, and it eliminates the toxins from your gastrointestinal tract
- It strengthens your immune system—lemons have a high level of Vitamin C which helps you keep colds at bay, a high level of potassium that stimulates your brain and the functions of your nervous system and they also help regulate your blood pressure
- It adjusts your body's pH level—lemons are some of the most alkaline foods you can consume.

Diseases are triggered by the fact that your body's pH level is acidic and not alkaline

- It improves the health and quality of your skin—the antioxidants and Vitamin C that are present in lemons help diminish wrinkles and skin spots
- It gives you a lot more energy and a feeling of well-being—lemons are the only known foods that contain negative ions, which help release all of the tension and negative energy that has built up inside your body. Moreover, the smell of lemons improves your mood and can also help diminish your anxiety and depression levels
- It freshens your breath and keeps your gums healthy—it protects against gingivitis and helps fight off toothaches

Note: It can, however, damage your teeth's enamel, so I recommend you drink this beverage using a straw and then rinse your mouth with some plain water.

How do you do this?

- Buy a water boiler that has an adjustable temperature setting and set the water to heat until it reaches 140 degrees F. The optimum temperature is somewhere between 122 degrees F and 140 degrees F. This may seem a bit unusual at first but, after a while, you'll get used to it and you'll start enjoying it. Warm water releases fresh energy into your body in comparison to cold water that sucks up energy (every food we eat that is below our body temperature is firstly heated through an energy-consuming process)

- Pour the warm water into a glass—preferably one that can hold between 10 fl. oz. and 13.5 fl. oz.—then add the juice from half a lemon and a half teaspoon of turmeric
- If you can't adjust the temperature of the boiler that you have at home, then boil 16 fl. oz. of water, then pour 2/3 of that hot water into a 16 fl. oz. glass and then add 1/3 of cold water
- Choose small- and medium-sized lemons that have thin skin and can be squeezed easily. Usually, large lemons have thick skin and less juice

Why should we add turmeric?

Turmeric offers you a number of specific benefits:

- It's an extremely powerful antioxidant that fights against the free radicals that are known to be carcinogens. It's especially used for its antiseptic and anti-inflammatory properties
- It's extremely good for your skin, irrespective

of whether you use it externally or internally. It cleanses, nourishes and hydrates the skin, maintaining its elasticity and youthfulness

- It's excellent for those wishing to lose weight. It helps eliminate the toxins that have accumulated in the liver and kidneys. It stimulates the absorption of nutrients inside the digestive system and regulates metabolism
- It's a natural bleaching agent. It's effective in reducing the appearance of skin spots and it also diminishes acne scars in just a few days
- It's the most common ingredient used in Ayurvedic medicine because of its anti-inflammatory properties

There's no other food ingredient that has such a powerful anti-inflammatory effect. The molecule responsible for this feature is curcumin.

C. THE HAWAIIAN MEDITATION

What is this?

Meditation, as I see it, is about quieting the mind and becoming aware of the present moment.

The mind possess this strange habit of being either in the past or in the future, and almost never in the present.

But the body is always in the present, so, becoming aware of the breathing is an easy way to stay in the 'here and now'. After trying many types of meditation, I came to the conclusion that the simplest and most effective is the Ho'oponopono meditation.

Dr Hew Len teaches Ho'oponopono which is the ancient Hawaiian system of healing, problem solving and transformation. You can read in detail about this system in the book *Zero Limits*.

Why is it great?

This is a very powerful technique that has brought peace and healing to me and many others. It's a great way to start the day, to clear all that is incomplete over the night and start fresh and energized.

Just as we shower on the outside, we need an internal shower to cleanse anxieties, frustrations and stress, and leave our body, mind and heart refreshed and ready for a great day.

How do you do this?

1. Relax with eyes closed. You don't need to be in a meditation position. It's OK to sit up with the back straight. You can even sit on a chair
2. Inhale through your nose gently while counting (count in your mind 1...2...3...4...5...6...7)

3. Hold your breath for seven seconds (count in your mind 1...2...3...4...5...6...7)
4. Exhale up to a count of seven (count in your mind 1...2...3...4...5...6...7)
5. Hold your breath for seven seconds (count in your mind 1...2...3...4...5...6...7)
6. Do this for seven minutes
7. Slowly open your eyes and notice how clear and balanced you feel!

Possible pitfalls and remedies

- Falling asleep: if it happens, don't worry. You just need more sleep. Plan to get at least an extra half an hour of sleep tonight
- Too many thoughts coming to mind: keep counting, because this way you will keep your mind from wandering
- No great improvements or 'a-ha' moments after the first sessions: it takes a few sittings to relax and quiet the mind. Give it time and your efforts will be rewarded

D. BODY TOUGH LOVE

What is this?

It's a strange but extremely effective exercise that involves light palm pats over the entire surface of your body, starting at the scalp and ending with your ankles.

Why is it great?

It's an excellent way to give your muscles a uniform energy boost. I personally practise this exercise not only in the morning but at noon and in the evening, and also when I feel I need to get more energy to my body.

An extremely important drawback of modern life is not being able to get in touch with the whole surface of our body on a daily basis. We have areas of our body that we totally ignore for days and even for weeks on end.

Other methods we can use to reconnect with our body are:

- Mindful shower, which is when you clean your body while paying close attention to your sense of touch throughout the shower
- Shower massage, which is when we focus on the area that's being massaged
- Guided relaxation, in which you consciously relax every part of your body

- Body tough love, which is the time when you cover your entire body with light and energizing palm pats

How can you practise this?[2]

- Reach out in front of you with your left hand (palm facing the ground) and then, with your right hand, begin to lightly tap your left hand starting from your shoulders and ending with your fingers (covering the entire surface of your hand do it thrice)
- Turn your left hand so that your palm is facing upwards and then, with your right hand, repeat the previous step (three repetitions)
- Then do the same with your right hand (three repetitions)
- Your chest (three repetitions)
- Each side of your waist (three repetitions)
- Your back (three repetitions)
- Your legs (front, back, outside and inside, each three repetitions)

---

[2]I have a video filmed for Body Tough Love. You may access it on my page on YouTube: https://www.youtube.com/user/danluca99/videos or https://www.youtube.com/watch?v=4nq77yRm4EM

After energizing your body through this exercise, take three deep breaths and raise your arms above your head. You will instantly feel like a brand new person.

After an initial adjustment period, if you want to reach a higher level, you can increase the number of taps from three to five or even 10 and you can also increase the intensity of these taps.

There are no side effects to this exercise and it's extremely motivating to observe the benefits immediately after practising it.

E. THE MIRACLE SHOWER AND THE TEST OF COURAGE

What is this?

It's an ingenious way to use your limited time in the morning in a more productive way.

In this case, it's about having a Bluetooth speaker in your shower, so that you can listen to audiobooks, TED talks or anything else while showering.

The test of courage refers to alternating between warm and cold water throughout the shower.

Why is it great?

This is truly great because you can sync your Bluetooth

speaker with your smartphone and, while your body gets refreshed, the mind can receive great nourishment right from the beginning of the day.

How can you do this?

It's quite easy. Go online to Amazon and order for the 'EcoXgear ECOXBT'.

You can hang it in the shower, using the hook that it comes with. It works on batteries so you don't have to worry about being close to a power/recharge outlet.

It works with iPhones and Android phones as well.

Send me a request at dan@5amcoaching.com and I will send you the MP_3 file with the shower incantation, which you can put on your phone and listen to it while you take your shower. The details of what you will find on this MP_3 file is in in the Morning Inspiration section from the Extras chapter at the end of the book.

During the first half of your shower you'll hear motivational affirmations and during the second half I encourage you to alternate between warm and cold water at least three times to wake your body up quickly and release the energy stored overnight.

Alternating between hot and cold showers has scientifically proven to be beneficial.[3]

---

[3]https://www.ncbi.nlm.nih.gov/pmc/articles/PMC4049052/

Start with a warm stream of water to receive the following benefits:

- Muscle relaxation
- Blood pressure reduction
- Decreased anxiety

Then continue and alternate the cold and hot water three times to receive the following benefits:

- Stimulate your immune system
- Increase your level of attention
- Stimulate your metabolism and the rapid release of energy
- Clear your mind

What does a 'hot and cold shower' actually mean?

A cold shower DOES NOT involve using cold water exclusively! It means diminishing the warm stream until the water temperature becomes uncomfortable but still manageable.

Count till 30 while you massage the entire surface of your body with cold water. Then again count till 30 while you increase the flow of warm water and regain your thermal comfort.

Repeat this transition three times and finish with a warm shower at a comfortable temperature.

After a while, you can increase the time you spend under the cold shower and decrease the temperature of the cold water.

Allow yourself to gradually progress without suffering from thermal shock.

Note: These warm and cold water transitions are not suited to people who have cardiovascular issues. Before undergoing this habit, check with your physician.

F. THE BEST BREAKFAST IN THE WORLD

What is this?

This breakfast is, actually, a smoothie. Why? Because it's fast, nutritious and delicious!

It's the best breakfast you can have in the morning so that you get your optimal dose of antioxidants and nutrients for an entire day. Moreover, it's the daily breakfast recommended by an MD, PhD with more than 30 years of clinical nutrition experience.

Why is it great?

The name of the excellent doctor I was talking about above is Dr Michael Greger, a physician, author and internationally renowned speaker on nutrition, food safety and public health issues.

He is a founding member of the American College of Lifestyle Medicine, and is licensed as a general practitioner specializing in clinical nutrition.

He is the founder of www.nutritionfacts.org, a website with more than 2 million visitors a month.

How can you make this great breakfast?

Use these ingredients:

- A cup of unsweetened almond milk
- A half cup of frozen blueberries
- The pulp of a ripe mango
- A tablespoon of ground flaxseeds
- A 'palmful' of white tea leaves
- A teaspoon of gooseberry powder

You can get all of these from a good supermarket, a Whole Foods Market or your local health food store or online at Amazon.

Put all the ingredients in a blender and mix them. You'll get approximately 17 ounces (or 500 ml) of smoothie.

The quickest and most comfortable blender you can use to prepare this go-to smoothie is Black&Decker.

Search Amazon for 'Fusion Blade Personal Blender'.

Another thing you can do to make your life easier is prepare 14 sachets filled with 100 per cent of all of the ingredients you will need. Thus, you will avoid preparing your smoothie using an incomplete recipe and you'll even avoid skipping a day because you haven't bought all of the ingredients.

I also invite you to watch the video that Dr Greger made on this topic on his website: www.nutritionfacts.org. Search for the video on his website using the phrase 'A better breakfast'.

G. JOURNALING

What is it?

It's the easiest way to stay connected to your true self, to the best version of yourself.

Why is it great?

It's an excellent habit since, as you probably already know, all the resources that you need are within you. Turn your attention inwards and find the significance of everything you do.

Journaling might also be called the act of thinking in writing.

A few years back, I heard a quote that I still remember every time I see my journal: 'Great ideas will visit you only once. You'd better capture them, or you'll lose them forever'.

How do you do it?

Answer the following questions in a nice journal. My absolute favourite is Moleskine. If you are not yet a fan, you should try it. I have given 31 questions to match maximum days in a month. You should answer the same question, for each particular day of a month for the next 12 months, and observe how your answer changes from month to month. For instance, on 5 January you answer question #5 and you'll also answer this question on 5 February, 5 March, etc.

1. What would I dare to do if I knew I could not fail?
2. What am I assuming about what's possible and impossible?
3. What hill am I willing to die on?
4. What brings me joy and fulfilment?
5. What revolution do I want to lead?
6. I imagine myself 12 months from now. What is one thing I'm glad I did?
7. What do I enjoy doing so much that I'm very good at and obtaining remarkable results?
8. Who do I admire? Who are my mentors? Why?
9. When was the last time I delivered more than was asked of me? What motivated me to do so?
10. When was the last time I lost track of time and entered a state of flux? What was I doing at the time?

11. What displeases me? What do I want to change in my environment?
12. Who is that one person that I would like to invite out to lunch? What questions would I ask that person?
13. What is the hobby that I would like to try? Why do I find it interesting?
14. When was the last time I got out of my comfort zone? What did I learn about myself?
15. When was the last time I was so excited about a project that I couldn't sleep at night because of my anticipation?
16. Who knows me best? What are the five things I believe that person would say about me?
17. Who would I like to get along with better? What could I do concretely to improve my relationship with that person?
18. What did I want to become when I was five years old? To what extent is what I'm doing right now related to that childhood dream?
19. If I were to write a book about my life that would help a lot of people, what would its title be and what chapters would it have?
20. Which type of charitable NGO would I allot two hours each week? What would I do exactly so that I may feel that my contribution is significant enough?
21. What's the oldest goal I haven't yet accomplished? Is

it still significant for me and do I still want to see it through or could I be ok if I never accomplished it?

22. Twenty years from now, CNN is doing a documentary about me. What is the title of that documentary and what are the three most important ideas regarding my life?
23. What are the things I'm grateful for?
24. For which activity have I doubled my productivity in the last 12 months?
25. What advice would my twenty-year-old version of myself give me now?
26. What is the event that will take place sometime during the next 30 days that I'm waiting for impatiently and why?
27. What do I think is the belief that's holding me back the most? How could I find evidence to disprove its validity (people, events, science, etc.)?
28. What is the habit that I would like to implement in the next 30 days and why?
29. What is the toxic habit I would like to get rid of in the next 30 days?
30. What could I learn during the next 30 days to double my income?
31. If, for just one day, I could have a superpower, what would it be and what would I use it for?

H. ONLY ONE

What is it?

It's an extreme method of prioritizing the schedule of a busy person. Instead of working on lots of small pieces and many projects at the same time, work on just one piece of the most important project of that particular day.

Why is it great?

A mind that concentrates on just one thing at a time tends to win the game every time. First of all, take the most important step. Forget everything else.

The days when I focus on just one thing are usually 2x to 5x more fruitful. My productivity level has skyrocketed and the quality of my work has exceeded even the highest standards I had.

How do you discover the most important goal of the day?

1. Make a list of five goals you would like to accomplish today
2. Open the www.onlyone.io application
3. Enter those five goals into the application
4. The application will have you compare these goals two at a time

5. Choose from each pair the most important objective
6. At the end, the application will generate your list of objectives based on the choices you have made but, most importantly, it will show you what your main goal for that day is
7. You then send the resulting list to your email address so that you have it handy and you are able to accomplish your goals in a predictable manner

Check the degree of relevance that the Daily Goal has for you.

Ask yourself the following questions

1. If today were the last day of my life, would I want to do what I am about to do today? If the answer is YES, go on (Steve Jobs used to ask himself this question every day).
2. Would I want to call my best friend at the end of the day and brag about this accomplishment?
3. Will this goal count five years from now?
4. What advice would 'X' (mentor) give me on accomplishing this goal?
5. How could I reach this goal for today if I worked for only one hour?
6. What is a completely different way of achieving this goal?

Possible pitfalls and remedies

Pressing matters to attend to: It's quite interesting, but when you work consistently on your #1 priority, you have way fewer fires to put out. So, this is a remedy in itself.

I. TWELVE-MONTH GOALS

What is this?

It's the most simple and effective method to clarify your goals for the next 12 months. It was invented by a mentor of mine and it has yet to be equaled with regards to its simplicity and effectiveness by any other method.

Why is this practice so special?

The wrong moment for setting our goals is when we feel extremely good.

This usually happens either at the beginning of the year—while we're still on holiday—or during a training session where the speaker makes sure we feel very excited.

The problem is that this particular state of mind will not repeat itself during the next 364 days of the year. Therefore, you're setting goals when your energy level is really high but you'll have to execute the necessary actions when your energy level is much, much lower.

The advantage that this technique provides is that by

writing and rewriting your goals on a daily basis, for 30 days, your internal negotiation process takes place over the course of many days and many different moods.

Hence, some of your goals might disappear because they're really not that relevant. Others will become essential to you while some of them will combine and give birth to even more important goals as well as many other combinations you'll discover during the process.

How do you do this?

Brian Tracy recommends the following process:

1. Grab an organizer or a special notebook (you can also use the same Moleskine notebook you rely on when you answer your daily question)
2. Write 12 goals you would like to accomplish during the next 12 months
3. Write these goals using the present tense, in the first person, and also set a time constraint (for instance, I am making sales worth $100,000 by 31 December)
4. Each morning, write your list of 12 goals WITHOUT looking at what you wrote the previous day
5. Repeat this process for the next 30 days and you'll notice how your goals will get sifted and the only ones remaining will be the ones that are truly important

J. THE RELATIONSHIP NOTE

What is this?

It's an easy and simple way of upgrading your relationship; a distinct gesture of appreciation at the beginning of the day that can really light things up for a couple.

Why is it great?

It is awesome because you only need five minutes (or less) to write a great note.

Do some soul searching and write something from the heart; write something that will brighten your spouse's day, write something that will bring a smile to the face of your loved one.

I'm sure that you know how great it is to feel the love of the most important person in your life. You feel invincible! This is why doing this for someone else is a great relationship enhancer!

How can you write this note?

You don't need to become a card writer for Hallmark or Archies. You don't even need to become a part-time writer. It's enough to choose from the questions that I will give you and answer them from your heart. That's it!

Here are some questions that you can answer and put them in the note

1. What compliment have you never made to your spouse?
2. What is one trait of your partner that you are glad he/she has, because you lack it?
3. In what way has your spouse surprised you pleasantly in the last few days? Why do you appreciate that?
4. What compliment would you like to receive from your spouse, so that you can offer it first or if you like something more straightforward, you can use one of these:
   - You inspire me
   - I love to hear you laugh
   - You are my biggest treasure; I feel rich every day!
   - Your gorgeous smile can lighten up my darkest day
   - You amaze me with your…
   - You light up my life
   - You have a beautiful soul
   - You are lovely in so many ways
   - I am the luckiest person alive when you hold my hand
   - I have butterflies in my stomach when you say my name
   - I love you not only for what you are, but for what I am when I am with you

Possible pitfalls and remedies

- Out of inspiration: Write more than one note on the 'inspired' days and keep them for the 'low-inspiration' days
- You stop writing because your spouse is not writing back to you: If you are willing to wait for a few more days, you will see some changes in your spouse's behaviour. But this is not the purpose of this practice. Do it because it makes you feel great and because you can show daily appreciation for the person you've chosen to be your spouse
- You are reluctant to repeat some of the 'greatest hits' from the previous days or weeks, you seek only new stuff: A belief is carved into our minds after many repetitions. So, actually, you are doing your spouse a favour by repeating some of the ones that had great impact on him or her. You reaffirm that you really believe that and it makes you feel grateful, often

You now know the most effective things to do as soon as you wake up in the morning. Let's now move on and see some of the key factors that will help you wake up early in the morning, so that you may use this time to do the Morning Ritual.

To conclude, from my perspective, a great morning routine or the first hour of the day needs to have some prerequisite conditions met:

1. It needs to be simple and easy to follow
2. It needs to have a natural progression
3. It needs to be accessible to any person not just the ones with unique environments and conditions
4. It needs to be pretty much the same every day so you can install all of it as a habit
5. It needs to be strictly timed so that you don't negotiate with yourself a lower version of it

I am confident that each of these prerequisites is met in my Morning Ritual.

And to be double sure, let me do a quick recap of them all.

1. You take care of the energy in your body with these habits:
   - Hot water with lemon and turmeric
   - Body Tough Love
   - The Miracle Shower
   - The Best Breakfast in the World
2. You take care of your clarity in your mind with these habits:
   - Only One
   - Twelve-Month Goals

3. You take care of your confidence level by addressing the emotional needs through these habits:
   - Journaling
   - The Relationship Note
4. You take care of your significance level by connecting to your values and higher aspirations with these habits:
   - Gratitude
   - The Hawaiian Meditation

In this way, you take care of most of your core needs from the first hour of the day and you are easily in the top 0.1 per cent of the people who start their day in terms of essential resources needed for a great day.

Do yourself the greatest good and give yourself the gift of the first hour, your life will be completely transformed in just a few weeks, as I have witnessed this first hand in my life and in the lives of thousands of the people that live like this now.

In the next chapter, I'll give my best reasons to motivate you to wake up at 5 a.m., and also the best two tools that will guarantee you success in implementing this life-changing habit.

CHAPTER THREE

THE 5 A.M. REVOLUTION

I started waking up at 5 a.m. on 2 October 2009… almost by mistake and I'm still waking up at 5 a.m. to this day, and don't intend to stop anytime soon.

I've been a long-time fan of Robin Sharma's 5 a.m. Club and I came in contact with this idea at least seven to eight times before it clicked into place.

I was aware of this idea long before that because my grandpa was a milkman and used to wake up at 4 a.m. to deliver milk. My father was an engineer who worked the first shift from 6 a.m.

I'll give you my method of waking up (perfected in the last nine years), but the method without a reason is worthless.

So before the **HOW**, you will need a **WHY**.

My grandpa and my father were my original inspiration, but with a twist.

They HAD TO wake up...but I WANTED TO wake up.

It's a big difference in the sense that 'when you don't have a choice...it's easy'.

When you don't have a choice but to feed your kid; it's easy to go to work to put bread on the table.

When you are sick and have to take a medicine, it's easy; you will take it without hesitation.

When you don't have a choice but to pay your mortgage, it's easy to put aside that money.

It's way harder when you don't HAVE TO...but you CHOOSE TO.

You don't have to read daily.

You don't have to eat greens every day.

You don't have to exercise daily.

You don't have to set your priorities every day.

(You 'don't have to' in a sense that in most cases no immediate adverse reaction will occur.)

and not lastly...

You don't have to Wake up at 5 a.m.

(not unless you work the first shift, have a small child to feed or have a long commute to work.)

But if you choose to wake up at 5 a.m., you need a

heck of a reason, because otherwise it won't last.

So what was my reason for waking up so early?

Having more than 500 clients whom I have coached, almost ALL of our conversations came to this same bump in the road: 'I don't have time to practise, to eat, to read, to be with my kids, to clear my head...' and so on.

'I know they could be good for me, but I just can't find the time'.

Keep these two things in mind:

Nothing changes until you change.
—Jim Rohn

'You will not change until you allocate dedicated time to practice so that the changes can take place.' —This is mine

There are a few people who do find little time for themselves. And most of these people take personal time in the evenings after everyone is asleep so they don't get interrupted. Usually, this time is after 10 p.m. and it can go for up to two to three hours.

This approach has at least three major inconveniences:

1. **You are tired after a full day's work and your willpower is at its minimum** and it's hardest to implement new habits that require a lot of energy.

(About 10 per cent of people are night owls, but most of us only think this is because he/she must have perpetuated bad habits from their early '20s.)

2. **You put yourself last.** I used to say that most people don't even get to play a small part in their own movie, let alone the leading role. You are at the bottom of the list and more times than not you are not even on your list altogether. This has a negative impact on your self-esteem because you fail to keep the promises you make to yourself.
3. **Your main focus is to finish the uncompleted tasks or projects and go to bed.** This is essentially a reactive energy that is looking to mainly 'land the plane'. But making personal changes require a different type of energy—a proactive one that is about 'taking off' and initiating new behaviour.

So if the evening time was not the answer…the morning time must be the right answer!

And indeed it was!

In the space of these two hours gained (5 a.m. to 7 a.m.), I was able to exercise, hydrate, breathe, meditate, read, plan, reflect, be grateful, write, etc.

This is my time to grow and expand and nobody can take that away from me. The kids are sleeping, the phone is not ringing, nobody sends me texts or emails…so it's just pure joy of starting each day in the best possible way.

Find your WHY and the HOW will be 100 times easier… because no HOW can compensate the lack of a proper WHY.

So, let me give you some ideas about what your 'why' could be.

A. FIFTY REASONS TO WAKE UP AT 5 A.M.

1. You become a one-percenter, the most productive group in the world! It's a select club and it's an honour to be a full member.
2. You have the opportunity to spend quality time with yourself; you put yourself first because you deserve it! You're the most important person in your life.
2. Nobody's awake at that time to bother you with phone calls, emails, texts, etc.
3. You can train for a marathon. In this sense, I really admire Andrei Rosu. He is featured in the Guinness Book of World Records as being the first one to complete seven marathons and seven ultramarathons in all the seven continents. In his own words, without waking up early in the morning, these achievements would have remained merely dreams, impossible to achieve.
5. You can create a strategic plan for your business (or your future business if you're still employed). If you don't do this in the morning when you feel rested,

when else? When you come home at night feeling drained?

6. You enjoy a tasty breakfast without feeling the rush of the cuckoo clock. Ah, the small pleasures in life…
7. You have the opportunity to see a sunrise. And I'm not talking about the one you see in pictures. I'm talking about the real one, one of the best free delights in life!
8. You can savour a cup of tea or coffee. I prefer tea. My favourite is the vanilla-flavoured Rooibos tea… priceless!
9. You can spend 30 to 60 minutes reading each day for the purpose of becoming an expert in your particular field! You can read between 50 and 100 books in just 300 days. Do you believe all this knowledge will make a difference five or 10 years from now? I'm sure it will!
10. You can watch inspirational videos like those posted on TED or those held by Robin Sharma, Tony Robbins, Randy Gage, Brian Tracy, etc. *Just one 'dose' of these types of videos a day can turn you into a different person and you then realize that excellence is a trait built over time and on a daily basis.*
11. You go out for a run without being disturbed by traffic. Priceless!
12. You have enough time to prepare and dress impeccably. Have you ever heard someone ask 'where did you put

my shirt, socks, belt, scarf, etc.?' Well, you'll be able to relax about all of these things.

13. *You can plan your priorities and this makes it easier for you to say 'no' when your coworkers, boss or friends demand unreasonable things from you. Why? Because you clearly know what you have to do on that day and how much free time you have available.*
14. You meditate in silence and solitude for five to 10 minutes, focusing on your breathing. This allows you to feel calm and relaxed.
15. You take a walk and enjoy the fresh morning air. We balance our inner system through movement. This is why 15 to 20 minutes of walking is pure gold!
16. You exercise and boost your metabolism. Therefore, you have enough energy after you wake up in the wee hours of the morning. You don't have to go to the gym. Ten minutes spent exercising at home are enough. I'm talking about deep breaths, stretching, jumping jacks, squats, sit-ups…nothing complicated.
17. You set your intentions regarding this new day that is about to unfold. The clearer your expectations are about what you wish to achieve, the more likely you are to obtain those results. Confusion can only lead to confusing results.
18. You start activities that you wouldn't deal with in the evening when you feel tired after a hard day at the

office. For example, you plan to start a new business, you learn a foreign language, you study a field in which you wish to become an expert, etc.

19. You call a friend and congratulate each other for waking up at such an hour and for being members of this select group of one-percenters. If you don't have a wake-up partner, you can find one who is a member of the 5 a.m. Club.
20. You can offer your consulting, coaching or mentoring services to a young man during your morning walk (without having to take any extra time out of your already planned day). Thus, you contribute to the development of a student without skipping your morning walk. What an excellent way to start your day!
21. You spend two extra productive hours working for your company without being interrupted and this allows you to double your efficiency. In this manner, you get to complete 25 to 50 per cent of your daily tasks. You will feel much more relaxed and confident knowing that you will finish everything you had planned for that day.
22. You can make breakfast for your spouse and family. Do you want to see smiles in the morning? This is the easiest way!
23. You repeat your affirmations in the mirror or while

you exercise: 'Everything I need lies within me now', 'I like myself just the way I am', 'I'm responsible', etc. You condition your mind to think in a way that supports you rather than sabotages you.

24. You choose the next conference or congress you want to attend in your area of expertise so that you are constantly prepared and up to date. It's your only chance to keep up with new trends.
25. You inhale essential oils—eucalyptus and mint—to open up your nasal passages and to place yourself into an excellent state in a very short amount of time. I never imagined the olfactory sense could have such a positive effect on my well-being.
26. You practise coaching—via phone or Skype—with clients who are top performers as well as one-percenters. I have been at it for more than five years and I have coached over 300 clients using sessions that start at 5 a.m. or 6 a.m. In my opinion, this is by far the best interval for this activity. It's quiet, nothing is causing us to be in a hurry and we are well-rested and have lots of energy (a result of our breakfast and physical exercises).
27. You listen to personal and professional development programmes and you set out to apply one or two techniques you heard. You develop your expertise and your confidence step by step.

28. You use photo reading to read one book every 30 minutes. It's a revolutionary technique, developed by Paul Scheele, that uses the whole brain to read and allows you to extract the essential knowledge from a book in the shortest time possible. It can literally change your life. I'm not kidding!
29. You write a greeting card for someone dear to you and you leave it on the refrigerator for them to find and read. It takes you about 20 seconds to do this. The effect: a positive mindset throughout the day (for you as well as for the recipient of the card).
30. *You start your day with proactive, rather than reactive, energy when you feel like you're running late from the second you get out of bed. If you want to have an increased level of control over your life every day, start by clarifying what's important and what's non-negotiable for you. And stop giving up on what's important to you!*
31. You have enough time to practise Ho'oponopono regarding the people you wish to have a more harmonious relationship with. Also called 'The Forgiveness Therapy', it consists of four affirmations: 'I'm sorry', 'Please forgive me', 'Thank you' and 'I love you'. All you have to do is repeat these four affirmations for a few minutes while thinking of the other person (an ideal session lasts 10 to 15 minutes

and produces rapid results).

32. You increase your level of energy by practising the four tempo breathing routine (four inhales followed by four deep exhales). Shallow breathing is quite common among those who spend a lot of time at the office. This is why deep breaths help you to quickly increase your level of energy.
33. You feel the need to have a hobby just for yourself: it could be painting, sculpting or photography. Do something each day to please your soul without forgetting who you are…start the day with yourself!
34. You have time to plan your dream summer vacation (and you can research the best offers available without feeling the pressure of time). When you have several hours to spend doing thorough research you will most likely save a serious amount of money.
35. You write your goals for the next 12 months on a daily basis for at least 30 days. Each day you write them on a separate page without looking back. In this way, you 'allow them to negotiate among themselves' their hierarchy based on how meaningful they are to you. I can guarantee some 'a-ha' moments.
36. You establish your top-five priorities that you have to finish that day. You estimate the necessary time to do so as well as envision the desired result.
37. You drink about 1 pound of water, recharge your

batteries and rehydrate yourself after a goodnight's sleep. My recommendation is that you drink water which has a temperature higher than that of your own body so that you don't consume extra energy to heat it up once it reaches the stomach.

38. You write for 15 minutes everything you feel grateful for, thus releasing any trace of anxiety. It's something easy to do that has a guaranteed positive effect throughout the day. You won't need sedatives anymore, you'll be releasing endorphins naturally!
39. You take the time necessary to create a board with pictures which represents the achievement of your goals. Some call it a Vision Board or a Dream Board.
40. For 10 to 20 minutes each morning you contemplate this board and fill yourself up with the emotion associated with achieving those specific goals. This will increase your level of clarity regarding why you're doing what you're doing and what's the final purpose towards which your efforts are oriented.
41. *You then use this positive emotion to plan and act in the direction of your goals. You enter a stage of inspired action. You no longer need willpower to do something. Inspiration tells you what actions are the right ones to do.*
42. You write the book you've always wanted to publish. Write one page each day. Christopher Hitchens once

said: 'Everyone has a book inside of them'. At the end of the year, you'll have written 365 pages. All done! Find a publishing house and publish your book!

43. *You write articles on your blog and you inspire other people to reach their potential. Let me give you a suggestion: stop keeping all of those great ideas only inside your head because the next ones won't have any room available! Write articles, write a book, and tell others. Do anything, just get them out of your head and into the world so that you can make room for the next great ideas to come!*
44. You remember the most important 10 victories—personal or professional—in the past 12 months. You fill yourself with confidence and you emanate this feeling through every inch of your body, thus inspiring everyone you meet. This way you'll become the person they always want to be around, because you have such a positive impact on others.
45. You leave for work on time and you reach the office feeling relaxed and smiling. The 10 minutes you use as backup save you the stress of countless red lights and traffic jams. A small investment for such a high reward!
46. You eliminate 95 per cent of the stress you're dealing with right now. As long as you combine a multitude of habits described above, you'll find yourself lacking

reasons to stress out. But don't take my word for it... try it for yourself!

47. *You gain the instant respect of anyone you share your story with. To many, your story is similar to running a marathon. It won't be long until people wonder how you are so calm, relaxed and confident. Then, with a wide smile on your face, you can ask them: 'Are you ready to hear what I'm about to tell you?'*
48. You start your day by putting yourself first, thus raising your level of self-esteem because you are the most important person in your life! I think it's obvious that if you first take care of yourself, you'll then be able to take care of others much better. You can't offer someone something you don't have enough of for yourself.
49. You are a select member of the 5 a.m. Club :)
50. You claim your power back, the power you conceded to external circumstances, thus becoming a centered, balanced and harmonious person who achieves everything he/she sets out to do because you have already solved your internal conflicts...the only ones that are truly relevant.

B. THE WAKE-UP PARTNER

If we are together, nothing is impossible. If we are divided, all will fail.

—Winston Churchill

What is one of the most important ways to make sure you are consistent with your purpose, which also works for waking up early, or when it comes to any other habit? Having a wake-up partner!

Surely you know the saying: 'Two is better than one.'

Why does it work? Because it addresses the main obstacle when it comes to adopting a new habit, inconsistency.

That is, today I will do what I set out to do…tomorrow I won't, I'll see if I'll feel like it two days from now, so on and so forth.

When you have a trustworthy partner, each of you can support each other during difficult times.

Best-case scenario, both people are motivated.

Less-happy scenario, one person is motivated and the other one is fighting a lack of motivation. At that point, the unmotivated person can find support in his partner and thus get through his difficult time.

In another, almost non-existent scenario, both people are unmotivated, you both realize this simultaneously and all it takes is just one day for you to start supporting one another and getting back to your good habits.

The method I'm talking about right now has been tested and retested on dozens of my coaching clients, and I can guarantee you that a wake-up partner will dramatically increase your odds of implementing this habit much more easily.

How to apply this principle

1. Find one person among your coworkers, friends, etc. who wants to wake up early in the morning!
2. Set a wake-up time
3. Establish your form of communication—phone call or SMS
4. Identify which one of you will be the person to initiate the contact during your first week. Then switch
5. Set the waiting interval after which, in case the designated person for the week does not call (for instance, if after five minutes that person doesn't call), the other person can call them or text them
6. Find two questions you can ask each other in the morning to help your brain wake up faster—questions such as: what was your most important achievement yesterday? What's your objective for today? Who are you going to meet today and what result do you want to obtain?
7. End every interaction with a positive greeting (Have a productive day! I hope you succeed in everything you've set out to do!)

C. THE WAKE-UP TRAINING

Steve Pavlina[4] has patented 'the training for waking up early'.

Practise getting up as soon as your alarm goes off. That's right—practise. But don't do it in the morning. Do it during the day when you're wide awake.

Go to your bedroom, and set the room conditions to match your desired wake-up time as best you can. Darken the room, or practise in the evening just after sunset so it's already dark. If you sleep in pyjamas, put them on. If you brush your teeth before bed, then brush your teeth. If you take off your glasses or contacts when you sleep, then take those off, too.

Set your alarm for a few minutes ahead. Lie down in bed just like you would if you were sleeping, and close your eyes. Get into your favourite sleeping position. Imagine it's early in the morning…a few minutes before your desired wake-up time. Pretend you're actually asleep. Visualize a dream location, or just zone out as best you can.

Now, when your alarm goes off, turn it off as fast as you can. Then take a deep breath to fully inflate your lungs, and stretch your limbs out in all directions for a

---

[4]Steve Pavlina is a renowned Self-Help Guru, and creator of Personal Development For Smart People, https://www.stevepavlina.com/

couple of seconds...like you're stretching during a yawn. Then sit up, plant your feet on the floor and stand up. Smile a big smile. Then proceed to do the very next action you'd like to do upon waking. For me, it's turning on the water kettle.

Now shake yourself off, restore the pre-waking conditions, return to bed, reset your alarm and repeat. Do this over and over and over until it becomes so automatic that you run through the whole ritual without thinking about it. If you have to subvocalize any of the steps (i.e. if you hear a mental voice coaching you on what to do), you're not there yet.

Feel free to devote several sessions over a period of days to this practice. Think of it as performing sets at the gym. Do one or two sets per day at different times...and perhaps three to 10 repetitions each time.

D. THE WAKE-UP PREPARATION

To succeed in waking up in the quickest and most harmonious way possible, it's necessary you make sure that the following two essential elements are available to you:

Personal motivations and essential resources

Personal motivations often do not only refer to the reasons, which you offer yourself for waking up earlier in the morning, but also to the degree of validity that these reasons possess over time.

Essential resources include those tangible and intangible elements you will use to implement this habit in your life.

To clarify the reasons as to why you want to wake up earlier in the morning and ingrain them even more, answer the following questions.

Who do I want to become? How would I describe myself?

- I'm a morning person □
- I'm someone who allots the most precious time interval to myself □
- I'm part of a very select group of successful people □
- I'm an active person and not a reactive one □

What limiting beliefs do I have at this time? Why do I think they're true?

- I'm more effective if I work during the night and I don't get enough rest if I wake up so early □
- I can't wake up in the morning because I'm not used to getting up before noon □
- I can't find the willpower to wake up so early □
- Not even the birds are singing at 5 a.m…I can't change my lifestyle to implement this habit □

What new beliefs could I adopt as affirmations that will help me evolve?

- I always wake up early and enjoy that particular day as much as I can ☐
- I always get out of bed after the alarm clock rings ☐
- I have a lot of energy and I feel very motivated because I wake up early in the morning ☐
- I wake up and I'm productive while others are still sleeping ☐

What is my profound need? Why would I adopt such a habit?

- I need to organize myself and my energy optimally to achieve all of my goals ☐
- I want to start the day by allotting time for myself because I'm the most important person in my life ☐
- I want to be a role model for my family and friends ☐
- I want to see how high I can go if I practise the habits of people who are already successful ☐

After finding your motivations and firmly ingraining the future that you want for yourself into your mind, it's time to clarify the resources you'll use to implement this habit as quickly as possible.

1. **The space and the necessary instruments**—I will start by making sure I have a clock that is not easy to press the snooze button. After that, I ensure that my Morning Ritual is clear and that I'm able to start it as soon as I wake up; I make the decision of waking up early the night before so I can avoid negotiating with myself in the morning; and I make sure that I sleep a minimum of seven hours every night. Otherwise, I won't be able to maintain this habit long-term.
2. **Rewards**—Every morning I revel in the sunrise, one of the simplest and most beautiful wonders of this life; every morning, after I have completed my entire Morning Ritual, I drink my favourite espresso; and at the end of each week that I manage to wake up every day at 5 a.m. I go to a spa.
3. **Visualizing the immediate and long-term benefits**—When I imagine myself waking up early, I'm full of energy. I'm highly productive and I succeed in everything that I set out to do that day. After five years of practising this habit, I have fulfilled even my wildest objectives.
4. **Defining exceptions**—The days when I haven't been able to sleep more than five hours the night before, and vacation days when I may socialize well after the optimum hour to go to sleep. Also, the days when I'm travelling for work purposes in areas with different time zones.

E. WHAT TO DO WHEN YOU MISS A DAY

To forgive is to set a prisoner free and discover that the prisoner was you.
—Lewis B. Smedes

It's very important that you come up with a plan that includes what you're going to do when, for various reasons, you end up skipping a day out of your schedule.

And this could be the morning when you didn't manage to get up on time or any other day from any 30-day sequence that you take on to implement a new habit.

I recommend the following three-step process

Step 1: Forgive yourself!
Forgive yourself for not being 'perfect' because nobody is.

Step 2: Get back on the horse as fast as you can!
Restart the sequence of 'good' days—days when you've practised the selected habit—as soon as possible.

Step 3: Measure your progress to eliminate regret over a lack of perfection.
You can use your growth and development as a source of motivation or you can keep being the prisoner of your frustrations, consuming the energy that could help you reach your destination.

Why is it important to follow this process?

Small setbacks are almost unavoidable and herein lies the trap most people fall prey to as they plan to implement productive habits.

They have a 'perfect streak' for a few days and afterwards they have a day when they don't practise their habit at all.

Because they lose their sense of perfection, they stop practising altogether and set out to restart this sequence of practising productive habits after a couple of days.

Sadly, these couple of days turn into 'never' for a lot of people.

The alternative is to accept your 'imperfection' but under no circumstance should you allow two consecutive days to go by without practising the habit. Resuming the sequence after just a single day of a break is much easier to do than after two or more days.

Things happen this way because, when implementing new habits, an undisputed law of physics applies: 'a body at rest tends to stay at rest and a body in motion tends to stay in motion'.

Implementing any habit is very similar to the start of movement of a train's engine. It consumes a lot of energy to start moving and takes a while until it catches some speed. However, after surpassing its initial inertia, it manages to reach a greater speed while consuming a lot less fuel. And it doesn't just reach a greater speed, it becomes unstoppable, which is what you actually want when it comes to your productive habits.

After a single missed day, your engine hasn't stopped yet but after two or more unsuccessful days, it's as if you had stopped the engine.

Therefore, you'll need to restart it and surpass the inertia of recommencing.

So far you have learned about the things that make up a great night's sleep. Then you discovered the 10-step Morning Ritual that will best equip you for the day ahead. And now you put together the puzzle of waking up early in the morning.

You are now ready to move on to the actual implementation of this way of living to make it a part of your everyday life. I have no doubt that your life will be impacted in ways beyond your imagination and you will experience an increase in productivity and balance akin to that of thousands of my clients. Let's do this!

CHAPTER FOUR

THE 8-WEEK SYSTEM

At this moment, after going through the first three stages—how to sleep better, the Morning Ritual and how to wake up early in the morning—you're ready to apply all of this information in a structured and fluent manner.

The idea that I started from was to offer you a process during which small changes are introduced, once every week for eight weeks. In doing so, you're able to progress and observe concrete results from one week to the next and, at the same time, you don't feel overwhelmed by their scale and complexity.

The place in your life that you find yourself right now is neither good nor bad. It's just a benchmark, which we take into account when estimating the necessary length of time for you to reach your desired place.

I recommend you apply the following structure

Every week, go to bed 10 minutes earlier and wake up 10 minutes earlier as well.

This means that after two weeks, you'll be going to bed 20 minutes earlier and waking up 20 minutes earlier, too. After eight weeks, you'll be happy for those extra 80 minutes you won in the morning by going to bed 80 minutes earlier. However, these adjustments to your bedtime and wake-up time require that you make sure that you sleep a minimum of seven and a maximum of eight hours each night.

Sleeping less than seven hours or more than eight hours will take its toll on your health.

Therefore, the first adjustment that you need to make is to ensure that you sleep for a minimum of seven hours each night. Every morning we'll introduce new steps from the Morning Ritual during those extra minutes you get by going to bed earlier and, in the end, you'll have won enough time to practise the routine completely.

The goal here is that you end up sleeping between 10 p.m. and 5 a.m., the most adequate time interval when it comes to our biorhythm and the ways in which our body functions and restores itself.

If you already exercise in the morning, I recommend

scheduling these activities after practicing the Morning Ritual in order to not negatively affect the progress you make from one week to the next.

In conclusion, after eight weeks you'll have 80 minutes in the morning, 47 of those will be used to practise the Morning Ritual and you'll also need an extra nine minutes to change from the habits from the routine. Those extra minutes that you're left with after practising the Morning Ritual can be used to listen to audiobooks. I suggest you use these extra minutes to listen to audiobooks as well as go for a short walk (10 or 24 minutes).

To listen to audiobooks, you can either use Audible from Amazon or subscribe to Blinkist and listen to detailed summaries of the books you would like to read but can't because you lack the time. Usually, an audio summary from Blinkist lasts between eight and 15 minutes, just right for your morning walk.

At the end of these eight weeks, which I will talk about next, it's essential that you continue to follow these principles

1. Keep going to bed, waking up 10 minutes earlier each week so that you'll eventually end up going to sleep at 10 p.m. and waking up at 5 a.m.
2. Depending on your starting hour, you might not need eight or more weeks to get to 5 a.m. If you started at

6 a.m., you need only six weeks. Regardless of your starting point, it is best to shift your wake-up time so that you get to 5 a.m. If you need more than eight weeks to get to 5 a.m., please continue to subtract 10 minutes from your wake-up time so you can start your Morning Ritual at 5 a.m. and reap all the benefits of this great habit.

3. Start your day with the Morning Ritual as soon as you wake up.
4. Use the extra time you gain in the morning—after practising the Morning Ritual—to get some fresh air while listening to audiobooks. If, after returning from your walk (or run), you still have some extra minutes left, you can use them to learn and develop new skills through video courses, webinars and other learning activities.
5. If, after a while, you feel the need to quicken up the pace on your walk, it's quite alright to start jogging lightly, but remember to take breaks and walk to catch your breath. It's also all right if you never run and just walk instead. The choice is up to you.

Now you're ready to take the first step of your first week.

A. START YOUR 8-WEEK JOURNEY TO YOUR BEST SELF: WEEK 1 (8-MINUTE ROUTINE)

This is a historical moment! You're about to start your eight-week journey after which your life will shift through barely perceivable changes, which you'll be implementing in 10-minute increments each day.

To start off as smoothly as possible, we'll begin with three very simple habits that take up just 10 minutes of your time.

Like we previously agreed, you went to bed last night 10 minutes earlier and now you've woken up 10 minutes earlier.

Step 1: Water—One minute

Drink 17 ounces (500 ml) of warm water with lemon and turmeric as soon as you wake up. The water temperature should be higher than that of your body because this will help you gain some energy without the need of cooling down your stomach. Use small sips over the course of 12 minutes. You don't have to finish the entire glass from the word go. You can take a few extra sips even after completing steps two and three (also remember the detailed explanation in the Morning Ritual section).

Step 2: Body Tough Love—Two minutes

It's very easy to start practising this habit after you've started drinking water because you can then implement this activity even if you're still in your pyjamas. All you have to do is to rub your palms together to get them warm and then massage your face, ears and scalp. Afterwards, through light but firm tapping, cover each part of your body to awaken your inner energy and refortify.

Start with your arms, then your torso (front and back), and finish with your legs.

Practise these movements three times (watch the descriptive video from this Morning Ritual section to remember the succession of the taps: https://www.youtube.com/user/danluca99/videos).

Step 3: Breakfast—Five minutes

As you very well know, breakfast has been the subject of research for many years for Dr Greger. He found the best breakfast to be actually a smoothie. Place all of the ingredients we described in the Morning Ritual section into the blender that we recommended and make yourself the first meal of the day in a pleasant and easy way. Then take a couple of minutes to quietly enjoy this mix of essential vitamins and minerals.

These are the first activities of the Morning Ritual and they were meant to take you just about 10 minutes to complete. If you can't practise these three activities in just 10 minutes from day one, it's alright. You'll become better and better at it as the days go by.

Next week I will be introducing you to a new habit that you most likely already practise. However, we will assign it a special meaning that will help you increase your energy level in the morning even quicker.

Have a productive first week and we'll meet again next week, won't we?

B. WEEK 2 (18-MINUTE ROUTINE)

I trust you had a great first week and you managed to implement the three habits I suggested.

You might have already noticed an increase in your personal energy. You're probably achieving better results throughout the day and in the evening, and it's most likely that you don't feel as tired as you once did.

During this week, you'll be going to bed and waking up 20 minutes earlier than how you used to do them at the beginning of this programme.

The routine I'm proposing for this week is the following:

Step 1: Water—One minute

Drink 17 ounces (500 ml) of warm water with lemon

and turmeric right after waking up. I think this process is already familiar to you and you're already appreciating the benefits it has regarding your energy levels.

Step 2: Body Tough Love—Two minutes

Awaken your latent energy through gentle but firm taps over the entire surface of your body.

Step 3: Shower—10 minutes

The novelty element I recommend you to apply during this week consists of taking a shower with two distinct differences (than what you were used to by now).

The first distinct element is the Test of the Courage—the alternation of warm water with cold water five minutes into your regular shower. I recommend maintaining the cold water temperature at an uncomfortable but not unbearable level and, also, don't turn on the cold water at full blast. Rinse your body with cold water for 30 seconds then resume showering with warm water for another 30 seconds. Repeat this cold–warm alternation twice.

Finish the shower session with water at a neutral temperature. If you have any health issues it is contraindicated for you to practise these 'warm water–hot water' alternations without consulting your physician.

The second distinct element I suggest is the Miracle Shower, which consists of a 10-minute audio (practically the entire time you're in the shower) that nourishes your mind with positive affirmations and perspectives in order for you to start your day feeling clean both on the inside and on the outside. If you plant good seeds in the morning, you'll be sure to collect good crops the entire day.

Step 4: Breakfast—Five minutes

The ingredients selected by Dr Greger are highly nourishing and full of vitamins and minerals. I'm sure you have already noticed the positive energy it provides for the first part of your day. Enjoy this quick and delicious breakfast.

This is the Morning Ritual version that uses up the 18 minutes that you earned by going to bed and waking up earlier.

Next week we'll be talking about implementing a habit for your mind that will allow you to start your day feeling highly motivated and focused on what matters most in your life.

Have a productive first week and we'll meet again next week!

C. WEEK 3 (21-MINUTE ROUTINE)

We have reached the third week of this programme that gradually changes your life 10 minutes at a time.

This week you'll earn 30 extra minutes by going to bed and waking up earlier.

But let's see how the Morning Routine looks like in the third week:

Step 1: Water—One minute

Drink 17 ounces (500 ml) of warm water with lemon and turmeric right after waking up. No surprise here! You're helping your body start the day perfectly.

Step 2: Body Tough Love—Two minutes

Allow your body to wake up faster and maintain its energy for the next couple of hours; gentle but firm taps from head to toe.

Step 3: Shower—10 minutes

Last week we gave a new meaning to this daily habit that up until this point only had a functional role. We added the three crossings from warm to cold and the 10-minute audio track that will nourish your mind and plant the necessary seeds for a successful day.

Step 4: Breakfast—Five minutes

Use Dr Greger's super recipe to get all of the necessary vitamins and minerals first thing in the morning. Use the recommended blender to quickly prepare this breakfast without any hassles.

Step 5: One Question—Three minutes

The novelty this week consists of introducing a question with the purpose of focusing your attention on a very important aspect in your life. To successfully implement this step, print out the 31 questions from step no. 7 of the Morning Ritual section and keep that piece of paper someplace that's easily accessible to you in the morning.

Each question is destined for a specific day of the month. Namely, on 8 January I invite you to answer question no. 8. On 15 January, I invite you to answer question no. 15, and so on and so forth. Also, notice how your answer changes from month to month. Remind yourself of the details of this habit through the Morning Ritual section.

This is the Morning Ritual version for the third week of this programme. I'm sure you're already feeling more and more confident about the results and that it's becoming easier and easier to maintain your consistency.

Next week, we will be implementing a habit that calms your mind and helps you achieve a focused and relaxed state.

Till next week!

D. WEEK 4 (28-MINUTE ROUTINE)

We've reached our fourth week. We're halfway into implementing the Morning Ritual, and I'm confident you're already practising the morning habits and feeling more relaxed and sure of yourself.

This week you're earning 40 extra minutes in the morning by going to bed and waking up 40 minutes earlier. What a wonderful thing it is to achieve increasingly spectacular results using incremental increases that last just 10 minutes!

Let's see how your Morning Routine looks like this week.

Step 1: Water—One minute

Drink 17 ounces (500 ml) of warm water with lemon and turmeric as soon as you wake up. Every great day starts with adequate hydration.

Step 2: The Hawaiian Meditation—Seven minutes

This week we are introducing this habit that helps you relax as well as increase your focus. Your mind needs to quiet down in order to process the multiple elements that had an impact on it that day. These seven minutes are necessary so that the experiences are incorporated. It's OK for your inner voice to take a break. If that voice isn't willing to stop talking then we'll give it something to do, something that will help the process.

This is why I recommend that you count till seven (in your mind) as you breathe in, again count till seven as you hold the breathe, count to seven as you breathe out and then count to seven as you hold your breath. If you can't reach seven from the start, it's alright. Count to whatever number is comfortable for you and, in time, you will reach seven. Please revise all of the details of this extremely useful habit in the Morning Ritual section.

Step 3: Body Tough Love—Two minutes

After the seven minutes of meditation, your mind is now relaxed as is your body. Help your body get going again with light taps over your entire body. You'll reach an irresistible combination of calm, relaxation and invigoration.

Step 4: Shower—10 minutes

Your body will reach an enviable state of well-being after taking that shower during which you alternated warm and hot water thrice and listened to that super-motivating audio track.

Step 5: Breakfast—Five minutes

The right ingredients quickly mixed and a light digestion

will ensure everything you need for an optimal period of 34 hours.

Step 6: One Question—Three minutes

Find out what date you're in. Look at the paper with the 31 questions. Answer the question corresponding to your current day and use this answer to increase the level of motivation for achieving what you set out to do that day.

This is the Morning Ritual for the fourth week.

The routine this week lasts 30 minutes but you've gained an extra 40 minutes by going to bed and waking up earlier. Use those extra 10 minutes to take a short walk during which you can listen to an audiobook or a summary of a book from Blinkist.

We'll see each other again next week when we'll talk about the instrument that helps you prioritize your actions for the current day. Have a productive week!

E. WEEK 5 (35-MINUTE ROUTINE)

We've now reached our fifth week and we are dedicated to the implementation of the Morning Ritual. This week you'll earn an extra 50 minutes by going to bed and waking up earlier than you did when you started this programme.

I'm convinced you've already acquired some very

good skills regarding habit implementation and that your results are something to be proud of. I congratulate you for the progress you've made so far!

Let's see how the routine looks in the fifth week:

Step 1: Water—One minute

Drink 17 ounces (500 ml) of warm water with lemon and turmeric

This is the simple recipe through which you offer your body a vital resource after seven hours of sleep and dehydration.

Step 2: Hawaiian Meditation—Seven minutes

You allot seven minutes to concentrate on your breathing and count till seven for the four stages—breathe in—hold breath—breath out—apnoea. You calm your mind and allow it to become alert and focused.

Step 3: Body Tough Love—Two minutes

You wake your body up through light taps and you get it ready for a successful day.

Step 4: Shower—10 minutes

You refresh your body by alternating warm water with cold water three times all the while refreshing your mind by listening to 10 minutes of an inspirational audio track.

Step 5: Breakfast—Five minutes

You place the ingredients for a super energetic morning in a blender, which you can then use as a vessel that you can use to drink this smoothie. It doesn't get any simpler or any better than that.

Step 6: Only One—Seven minutes

This week's novelty consists of a software that helps you prioritize your to-do list. Access http://onlyone.io, and introduce the 57 tasks you wish to do on that particular day and then you compare these tasks, as pairs of two, to have a better hierarchy of their importance. Afterwards, email this list to yourself so as to easily monitor your progress throughout that day. Make sure that your evening routine also includes a daily review because this will help you make better decisions from day to day.

7. Step 7: One Question—Three minutes

Read the list of 31 questions. Identify the present date. Answer the question of the day and think about the existing connection between your response and your number one priority discovered during the previous step. Is the connection harmonious, conflicting or is there no connection at all?

This is the 35-minute version of the Morning Ritual.

Next week we'll be talking about a very short but powerful habit that has the ability to turn anxiety into happiness in just a couple of minutes.

During this week you've earned an extra 50 minutes. Since the Morning Ritual lasts 35 minutes, you're going to be left with another 15 minutes during which you can go for a walk and listen to audiobooks or book summaries from Blinkist. If you so desire, you can step up the pace on your walk or even start jogging lightly. It's up to you.

Have a productive week and you'll be hearing from me this coming week.

F. WEEK 6 (37-MINUTE ROUTINE)

We have now reached the sixth week and I trust you've consistently progressed from one week to the next. This is the week during which you gain a full hour considering where you were when you started this programme.

Instead of experiencing another late night, feeling tired and wanting to go to bed but finding different reasons not to, you've chosen to wake up earlier, start the day with yourself and gain enough energy and clarity for the entire day. Congratulations!

Let's see how the sixth week looks like.

Step 1: Gratitude—Two minutes

We're starting off the week with a new habit that's actually quite simple to practise. If I were to ask you what you are grateful for you'd certainly be able to offer me numerous reasons. But if I don't ask you, days or even weeks might go by without you remembering to take the time to be grateful.

This is why I've found a simple and handy method: write the five reasons you are grateful on a post-it and stick it to your bathroom mirror. This way, when you brush your teeth, you'll remember and it becomes easier to connect to the things that are valuable in your life. After 23 days you can change the post-it with another one on which you write other important things in your life. It's easy to express your gratitude but, at the same time, it's also easy not to.

Step 2: Water—One minute

Drink 17 ounces (500 ml) of warm water with lemon and turmeric as soon as you wake up. I think this habit has already become your second nature. It has in my case and ever since, I can't imagine any morning without my glass of warm water, lemon and turmeric.

Step 3: Hawaiian Meditation—Seven minutes

Seven minutes of calm and tranquility for your mind. It's the moment when your mind connects with your body in the here and now and stops running in the past or future. YOU ARE HERE.

Step 4: Body Tough Love—Two minutes

After a process designed to calm, relax and strike a balance, it's time to jump-start our metabolism and to release energy quickly throughout the entire body. Gentle but firm taps on your entire body wake you up and kick-start your day.

Step 5: Shower—10 minutes

After waking up your body with gentle but firm taps accentuate the invigorating feeling by alternating warm water and cold water for three crossings while your mind has its 'breakfast' that encompasses different ideas and inspirational attitudes.

Step 6: Breakfast—Five minutes

In just a few short minutes your smoothie is done and you receive the necessary energy for the next three to four hours. It is easy to make and easy to assimilate.

Step 7: Only one—Seven minutes

You access the software using the following link: http://onlyone.io/#/add. Afterwards, you create a hierarchy for your priorities. When you start your work day, you'll work at task number one until you've finished it and then you move on to task number two...and so on and so forth.

Step 8: One Question—Three minutes

This is a simple habit that connects you to your profound motivation. Check the calendar and notice the current date. Read the question that corresponds to that day and answer in such a way that you increase your level of motivation for the day ahead.

This is the 37-minute Morning Routine from the sixth week. Use the extra 23, or up to 60, minutes for a light walk or a run. Combine these exercises with an audiobook or a Blinkist summary to really increase the productivity of these extra minutes.

I wish you a productive day and you'll be hearing from me next week!

G. WEEK 7 (43-MINUTE ROUTINE)

We have now reached the seventh week of the programme that will help you implement the Morning Ritual. We're approaching the end of these eight weeks and I believe you've progressed.

Let's see how the routine is shaping up this week:

Step 1: Gratitude—Two minutes

Use a post-it and write five things you're grateful for. Stick this post-it on the bathroom mirror and practise gratitude as you brush your teeth in the morning.

Step 2: Water—One minute

Drink 17 ounces (500 ml) of warm water with lemon and turmeric as soon as you wake up. What would your morning look like without this habit? You probably can't even imagine. Hydrate your body and it will thank you for it!

Step 3: Hawaiian Meditation—Seven minutes

Allot seven minutes for your mind to quiet down and relax. It's the perfect way to begin the day with a maximum of clarity and focus. Give yourself this gift every morning.

Step 4: Body Tough Love—Two minutes

You energize your body through gentle but firm taps. You increase your energy level and you start your metabolism in just a couple of minutes.

Step 5: Shower—10 minutes

You continue increasing your energy and prolong the beneficial effects of the previous step. You take a 10-minute shower and alternate warm water with cold water thrice to invigorate. This temperature difference wakes you up and activates your immune system. Your body becomes almost invincible and your mind benefits from a special treatment with the help of the 10-minute audio track filled with inspirational ideas.

Step 6: Breakfast—Five minutes

Dr Greger's brilliant recipe can be mixed with the help of a blender that's easy to use. You prepare your breakfast in less than a minute but you have the necessary energy for the following 34 hours!

Step 7 Only One—Seven minutes

If you use this software, you avoid having those so-called under-productive days because Only One helps you separate the important tasks from the non-important ones. Access http://onlyone.io/#/add and prioritize your to-do list.

Step 8: One Question—Three minutes

Take the piece of paper on which you've written the 31

questions and answer the question for the day. Use a Moleskine notebook to write down the answer. This way, in a month or six months, you'll be able to compare the answers to the same question.

Step 9: 12 Goals—Six minutes

This process invented by Brian Tracy is extremely powerful. Use the same Moleskine notebook to write down the most important 12 goals for the following 12 months. Write these goals every day without looking back to see what you wrote in previous nap. This is how you can make sure that only the relevant goals are kept from one day to the next one.

This version of the Morning Ritual requires 43 minutes for completion. During this week, you've earned about 70 extra minutes taking into account your starting point.

Those 27 unused minutes can be spent on a walk or, if you're in a good physical shape, you can even run for 5 km. In any case, you can use headphones to listen to an audiobook.

Have a productive week and we'll see each other next week—the last of this 8-week programme. Hope you'll be there!

H. WEEK 8 (47-MINUTE ROUTINE)

We have reached the final week of the programme designed to help you implement the Morning Routine. From my own experience as well as that of my clients, I can tell you that these weeks have not been easy but they certainly have been easier than you might have expected.

Small incremental changes—in this case 10-minute changes—have the 'gift' of tricking our inner resistance to change until the benefits of that change become obvious.

During this week, you've earned 80 extra minutes of high-quality productivity instead of wasting those 80 extra minutes late at night with less satisfying activities.

Let's see how the complete Morning Ritual looks like.

Step 1: Gratitude—Two minutes

Write down the five things you're grateful for on a post-it and stick it on the bathroom mirror. While you brush your teeth in the morning, use this time to practise gratitude.

Step 2: Water—One minute

Drink 17 ounces (500 ml) of warm water with lemon and turmeric as soon as you wake up. The water temperature should be above that of your body.

Step 3: Hawaiian Meditation—Seven minutes

Concentrate on your breathing while you count to seven when you breathe in and out. Also do the same during the two intermediate moments when you're holding your breath and you're in apnoea, and there's no more air in your lungs. Relax your mind and connect it with your body in the HERE and NOW.

Step 4: Body Tough Love—Two minutes

Increase your level of energy and start your metabolism through small taps over the entire surface of your body. These taps are gentle but firm. After a while, this process should become natural to you and you'll begin increasing the intensity of the taps for a superior invigoration.

Step 5: Shower—10 minutes

You can increase the level at which your body refreshes itself each morning by alternating warm and hot water three times. The temperature difference will wake the body up from its dizziness. As you shower, listen to audio tracks of inspirational ideas to start your day on a perfect note.

Step 6: Breakfast—Five minutes

Dr Greger has invented the perfect method for having

enough energy for the first 34 hours after waking up in the morning. Prepare your ingredients ahead of time, put them in a blender and then enjoy a smoothie that has the highest density of vitamins and minerals.

Step 7: Only One—Seven minutes

By doing this, you'll eliminate the temptation of working on less important goals. Access: http://onlyone.io/#/add, create the hierarchy of activities for a particular day and then make sure you begin with your number-one priority.

Step 8: One Question—Three minutes

You look at the list of 31 questions and find the question of the day. Answer it and think about the possible connection between your answer and your number-one priority that day. Look for ways in which you can harmonize the two on a daily basis because this will increase the quality of your life.

Step 9: 12 Goals—Six minutes

Use Brian Tracy's method to clearly identify your goals for the next 12 months. Write the most important goals in the morning on your Moleskine notebook without looking at the ones from previous days. In the next few weeks only those goals that are truly important will remain.

Step 10: Relationship Note—Four minutes

This habit is essentially simple and pays of spectacularly but it's also easy not to practise the habit. Write a short message on a post-it for your spouse and leave it someplace he'll find that morning or throughout the day. Notice how the quality of your relationship begins to improve. For more details please review the information from the Morning Ritual chapter.

This was the eighth week. I trust you've progressed consistently and that you can now say that you've implemented a morning routine that will allow you to have more energy and clarity first thing in the morning.

Let me remind you of the principles you should keep in mind after finishing these eight weeks:

1. Keep going to bed and waking up 10 minutes earlier each week so that you'll eventually end up going to sleep at 10 p.m. and waking up at 5 a.m.
2. Start your day with the Morning Ritual right after waking up.
3. Use the extra time you earn in the morning—after practising the Morning Ritual—to get some fresh air while listening to audiobooks. If after returning from your walk (or run) you still have some extra minutes left, you can use them to learn and develop new skills

through video courses, webinars and other learning-related activities.

4. If after a while you feel the need to quicken up the pace during your walk, it's quite alright to start jogging lightly but remember to take breaks and walk so as to catch your breath. It's also alright if you never run and just walk instead. The choice is up to you.
5. After reaching the point of going to sleep at 10 p.m., waking up at 5 a.m. and practising the Morning Ritual, maintain this rhythm and enjoy your reward day after day.

Congratulations for your endurance and consistency. If you've made it up to this point I'm convinced that the benefits of this lifestyle are obvious.

I wish you have a journey filled with accomplishments as you continue and I promise to meet again with other learning opportunities!

Make sure to check out the 'extras' section so you get additional resources and unadvertised bonuses.

THANK YOU!

Before you go, I'd like to say thank you for purchasing my book.

I know you could have picked from dozens of books on habit development, but you took a chance with my system.

I'd love to hear your opinion about my book. In the world of book publishing, there are few things more valuable than honest reviews from a wide variety of readers.

Your review will help other readers find out whether my book is for them or not. It will also help me reach more readers by increasing the visibility of the book.

P.S. While it's 'easy' to connect over Facebook, Twitter or other social media sites, often it's better to have one-on-one conversations with readers like you. So I encourage you to reach out over email and say Hi!

Simply write here: dan@5amcoaching.com

To get started, I would love to hear about the one thing you'll do this week to turn this information into action.

Dan Luca
http://www.5amhacks.com

EXTRAS

A. MORNING INSPIRATION

Following are the Morning Inspiration to be used while taking the hot–cold shower. I also have audio files with me reading them, which I mentioned that I can share with you if you email me requesting these.

Let's begin…by reading out loud these statements in the morning:

1. This is a great morning! I am so grateful to be alive today
2. Every day I wake up with a smile on my face and joy in my heart
3. I begin this new day with a wonderful feeling of peace and gratitude
4. I am grateful and content with my life

5. I have been very blessed in this lifetime
6. I am proud of what I have achieved in my life
7. I am thankful that I get to live another day
8. Today is going to be a great day!
9. I am a new person today—better, healthier and happier than ever before
10. I wake up happy and productive. I trust myself and my decisions
11. I am at peace with all that has happened, is happening and will happen
12. I am in the best place possible to get from here to where I want to go

I now turn my attention to my body:

Body

1. I feel great today
2. I look great today
3. I feel strong today
4. I stretch and feel my body waking up
5. I love my body!
6. My body is the temple of my soul and I take great care of it
7. My body is healing and improving every day
8. Every morning I am refreshed and renewed and ready to start my day

9. I bring great energy to all things I do
10. My body is healthy, my mind is brilliant and my soul is serene

I now turn my attention to my mind:

Mind

1. My mind has unlimited power
2. I trust myself and my decisions
3. I am disciplined and productive in everything that I do
4. I become more productive every single day
5. I value my time, therefore I spend it wisely
6. My mind is focused like a laser
7. Today, I abandon my old habits and take up new, more positive ones
8. I always win because I am willing to work harder and smarter than anyone else
9. My income is continuously increasing
10. I always have enough money to suit my needs
11. Money flows freely and abundantly into my life
12. I am rich in health, wealth and love

I now turn my attention to my emotions:

Emotions and relations

1. My life overflows with happiness and love

2. I love and accept myself. I love myself more every day
3. I am worthy of happiness and respect
4. I am loved, loving and lovable
5. I surround myself with positive and loving people
6. I am fun and energetic and people love me for it
7. I choose to see the best side of people and circumstances
8. I am blessed with an incredible family and wonderful friends
9. I am thankful that I get to share this beautiful life with my partner
10. I take the time to show my family and friends that I care about them

I now turn my attention to my soul:

Spirit, soul, self

1. I believe in myself. Today, and every day, I choose to be confident
2. I am in charge of my life
3. I have the courage to make this a great day
4. I allow myself to play and enjoy life
5. I am making a difference in this world
6. I lead by example
7. I inspire others to be their best self
8. My everyday work has meaning and purpose

9. Everything works out for my highest good
10. The more I give to the world, the more I get
11. I always have everything I need to be happy

I now turn my attention to the future:

1. I am safe. All is well. Everything comes to me at the right time
2. I deserve whatever good comes my way today
3. I courageously open and move through every door of opportunity
4. I act with courage and confidence
5. I am always in the right place at the right time
6. I have everything I need to overcome today's challenges
7. I love facing challenges—they allow me to grow
8. Everything that is happening now is happening for my ultimate good
9. I live a positive life and only attract the best in my life
10. I learn and grow from every experience
11. I am looking forward to having a really great day
12. Every day in every way I am getting better and better

I am now getting ready for the 30-second cold and hot intervals.

I will turn on more cold water in 5…4…3…2…1… and my mantra is…

(30 sec session) × 7-8 times (cold water)

I like myself
I like my work
I can do it
I am responsible

I turn on more warm water in 5…4…3…2…1… and my mantra is…

(30 sec session) x 5-6 times (warm water)

I relax all my muscles and let go of any tension
I let the water clear any anxiety or fear
I am flexible and flowing like water
I feel loved
I feel protected
I am my best friend
I love and accept myself

I will turn on more cold water in 5…4…3…2…1… and my mantra is…

(30 sec session) x 9-10 times (cold water)

I am a genius and I apply my wisdom
I turn on more warm water in 5…4…3…2…1… and my mantra is…

(30 sec session) x 5-6 times (warm water)

I relax all my muscles and let go of any tension
I let the water clear any anxiety or fear
I am flexible and flowing like water
I feel loved
I feel protected
I am my best friend
I love and accept myself

I will turn on more cold water in 5…4…3…2…1… and my mantra is…

(30 sec session) x 5-6 times (cold water)

I am grateful
I am loving
I am inspired
I am enthusiast

I turn on more warm water in 5…4…3…2…1… and my mantra is…

(30 sec session) x 5-6 times (warm water)

I relax all my muscles and let go of any tension
I let the water clear any anxiety or fear
I am flexible and flowing like water
I feel loved

I feel protected
I am my best friend
All that I need is within me now
I am the architect of my life
I love and accept myself
I am healthy, wealthy, happy and wise
This was good
I am ready for greatness
Let's begin!

B. USEFUL GADGETS FOR WAKING UP EASIER

So, to be crystal clear, I am not receiving any commissions, so I am doing this purely because I believe in the benefits that these gadgets can have in helping you wake up easily and being refreshed.

1. Wake-Up Light (Amazon, search for 'Wake-Up Light', Philips)

Here's how it works: You set the time you want to get up, and the Wake-Up Light starts beeping at that time—softly at first, then louder after a minute and a half.

A half an hour before that, a simulated sunrise has already started, transitioning from a dim glow to full brightness.

By the time the sound kicks in, your room is all lit

up like it's early afternoon on a weekend. And this light intensity is scientifically proven to be the best way to wake up with.

The price range is between $70 and 170.

2. Aroma Diffuser and Sound Therapy Clock (Amazon, search for 'Oregon Scientific')

Here's how it works: It provides a gentle, soothing way to wind down after your day. Combining sight, sound and fragrance, the Aroma Diffuser and Sound Therapy Clock allows your evening to continue without harsh beeps, blaring music or jarring lights. The nature sounds and soothing, colour-changing light combine with a nice fragrance mist to create a multi-sensory experience.

The Aroma Diffuser activates your senses to soothe and invigorate your mind, body and spirit. This unique product harnesses three types of alternative medicine—aromatherapy, light therapy and sound therapy—to create a naturally pleasing environment that can positively alter your mood, cognition and overall health.

The price range is between $70 and 100.

3. Talk to a stranger to wake up (Google.com, search for 'Wakie' app)

Here's how it works: You are actually tapping into the app's community of users so that you can have a stranger from somewhere else in the world wake you up at a specified time (and vice versa, if you so wish).

It's anonymous and free (because everyone's volunteering), and the calls are automatically cut off after one minute, so the awkward small talk is kept to a minimum. Get up on time, and meet someone new as well, all before breakfast!

The app is free and it is available for Android and iOS.

4. Mind puzzles and exercises to wake up (Google.com, search for 'I can't wake up!')

Here's how it works: With this alarm clock you will get up on time, thanks to up to eight different Wake-Up Tasks, which won't let you turn the alarm off or lower the volume until you finish them!

You have up to eight different Wake-Up Tasks to perform after the first buzz: Math, Memory, Rewrite, Order, Pairs, Repeat, Shake and Barcode.

Additionally, you also have the Innovative Barcode Task option. All you have to do is scan a previously prepared barcode (from a toothpaste or a book) to finish a task and for that you need to get out of bed!

The app is free and it is available for Android and iOS.

C. FREQUENTLY ASKED QUESTIONS

1. Even if I get to bed at 10 p.m., I will just lay awake in bed for a few hours without actually sleeping. I am not tired at 10 p.m.

It is actually normal for this to happen because your body has adjusted to your current lifestyle. It's only natural to plan a transition to a new state step by step. Use the 8-Week System to transition from your current bedtime to the desired one.

You can very easily gain two hours of good sleep at night and two great hours in the morning in 12 weeks by only going to bed 10 minutes earlier per week. This is a small change to make without any considerable effort. But the cumulative effect is nothing short of a small miracle.

2. If I go to bed this early, will I lose all of my friends? Do I have to give up my social life?

No, you don't have to lose your friends and you don't have to give up your social life.

You will have to make some adjustments, but from my personal experience it is highly doable.

Let's say that a normal frequency for going out is two nights (or less) per week. During these nights you plan on staying up beyond the 10 p.m. bedtime.

To have the least impact on your sleep pattern, you can go out Friday and Saturday night. The rule is to sleep for seven hours from the time you hit the pillow. In this way, you don't get sleep deprived and you don't start the week on Monday feeling extra tired.

The reset time is Sunday evening. The key point to having this system work out is to get to sleep on Sunday evening at 10 p.m. Even if you don't fall asleep right away you will get rest for your body. Don't be annoyed if you stay in bed awake, use some of the relaxation techniques from the evening routine to fall asleep more easily.

The next key point is waking up on Monday morning at the preset time and not sleeping in. If you miss Monday morning wake-up time, it will be more difficult to get back in the rhythm.

If you had at least one night out over the weekend, it is highly recommended to avoid afternoon naps longer than 20 minutes. If you sleep longer, you'll not fall asleep as easily on Sunday evening, and this will impact your whole week's sleeping pattern.

Do it as described above and you can have it both ways: being an early riser and going out two nights per week.

3. When it comes to getting a good night's rest and waking up refreshed should we exercise in the morning or in the evening?

I recommend you exercise in the morning for various reasons:

- It's an easy way to stimulate your body to 'wake up' in the morning because physical activity gets your blood flowing and increases your heart rate. Thus it becomes easier for you to make the transition between the state of drowsiness you experience after waking up to the state of alertness you need for the activities you're going to perform during that day.
- Moderate physical exercise helps your body release serotonin, the 'feel-good' hormone that fights against depression and aids you in starting your day in the best possible way.
- Exercising at least three hours before bedtime is not recommended because your body temperature will rise, your brain will be oxygenated and activated; therefore, you'll find it difficult to go to sleep because you'll have an excess of energy that you haven't used up.

To conclude, the benefits that physical exercise brings you—a high level of energy and a good mood—are more useful for you in the morning, when you have to start your day en force, rather than in the evening, when you need to achieve a state of relaxation that will help you go to sleep.

4. What is the best position recommended for a restful sleep: on your belly, on your side or on your back?

The best position to sleep is on your back because it relieves backaches and neck pain and because it doesn't put pressure on your internal organs.

Also, this position helps reduce the symptoms of acid reflux disease because the stomach is situated higher than the oesophagus, given the slightly raised position of your head, and the stomach acid and ingested foods can't move up into your oesophagus.

For women, this is a great sleeping position, especially when it comes to their 'beauty' sleep since sleeping on your back helps you avoid wrinkles and maintain the shape of your breasts.

For people who snore, this isn't the best sleeping position. Sleeping on your side is recommended in this case. Health-wise, the least recommended sleeping position is on your belly.

5. What can we do so that our entire family—both adults as well as children—can manage to be 'in bed,

sleeping' during the recommended time interval in the evening (between 9.30 p.m. and 10 p.m.) in order to wake up at 5 a.m. to become sustainable for the adults?

The single best thing you can do for yourself and your family is to establish a bedtime routine. Small children already have this routine (eating dinner, putting their toys away, listening to a bedtime story, saying their prayers, etc.) but adults seem to have forgotten these repetitive and consistent activities that inform our brain that it's time to get ready for bed.

When you and your partner set up a routine together that involves the kids as well, I guarantee you'll be able to go to sleep at the hour you want.

This bedtime routine includes activities that help both your mind and body to relax, as well as aid you in detaching yourself from all the fuss and flutter of that particular day that's now ending.

6. What arguments can I present to my partner in order for him to become aware of the fact that going to bed and waking up earlier will help create an extraordinary life for ourselves?

The arguments in favour of going to bed and waking up earlier as well as the benefits of restful sleep can be found in the programme.

What I would like to point out, however, is that the

power of personal example is stronger than any argument you might present him or her with.

I recommend that you start going to bed and waking up earlier so that you can experience the benefits for yourself and then share your experience with your spouse.

The results you achieve during the time you spend with yourself in the morning, quality sleep and the state of well-being you experience the next day are just some of the arguments you'll be able to bring to the table.

7. As a parent, what habits could I teach my children (I have two boys—a six-year old and a nine-year old) to encourage them to choose this lifestyle in the future as well?

Children really have a tendency to model their parents' behaviour. If you can manage to be disciplined and organized, then these traits will also influence how you interact with your children, and thus they will model this behaviour as well.

The simplest method to achieve your goal is to mould your children through the activities you practise together. Establish a mealtime routine, a bedtime routine and a morning routine where your kids wake up at the same hour every morning. Implement habits alongside them:

- Every evening, after dinner, go for a short walk through the park
- Every weekend try something new together; like visit a new place
- Every night say your prayers together
- Every morning wish yourselves a beautiful day
- Every evening identify at least five things you're grateful for

The simplest, yet the most difficult method of teaching young children is through personal example.

8. Is the famous 'snooze' button on your alarm clock as harmful as they say?

If you want to implement the habit of waking up early in the morning you need to make this decision the previous evening, before going to bed, while you're still consciously in charge of your own decisions.

When you don't make this decision the previous evening, you're actually leaving it up to a sleepy person who only wants to avoid any activities and stay in bed because it's nice, warm and cozy.

What decision do you honestly think you'll make under these circumstances? You'll decide to go back to sleep…

When you first hit the snooze button, you give

into temptation for the first time. You haven't followed through with your decision, you've allowed yourself to start negotiating with your subconscious and you end up losing the battle.

The more times you hit the snooze button, the lower your self-esteem goes because you're telling your brain that you're not able to respect your decisions.

Every morning you give up on waking up as soon as the alarm goes off diminishes your chances of implementing this habit successfully in the future as well, not just on that particular day.

The reverse is equally valid. If you wake up in the morning as soon as the alarm goes off you'll feel great because you'll have respected your decision. You'll feel a deep sense of satisfaction and your brain will want to hang on to this behaviour because it leads to instant gratification.

When your body hears the alarm go off it starts to wake up and eliminate the analgesics that were maintaining the state of sleepiness. By remaining in bed, you're forcing your body to start secreting these analgesics again and it'll go back to sleep.

This is why, when you sleep just a little bit more, you get out of bed and feel like you've been hit by a car. Your body is sedated because you forced it to secrete analgesics by putting off getting out of bed.

To conclude, you'll feel much better if you wake up and get out of bed on time—even if you've not slept enough—rather than hitting snooze and then getting out of bed. Now that you know this, perhaps you'll make a firm decision in the evening to get out of bed the following morning as soon as you hear the alarm clock go off.

9. I have a pretty young child that still wakes up at night and goes to bed fairly late (1 a.m.). Under these circumstances can I still implement the habit of waking up at 5 a.m.?

As long as this situation is not an exception, meaning it will repeat itself over a long period of time in the future, it's not at all feasible for you to wake up at 5 a.m.

You need to make sure that you sleep at least seven hours each night, ideally without interruptions. Going to bed at 1 a.m. doesn't provide you with the resources necessary to sustain the habit of waking up early in the morning.

Waking up at 5 a.m. is not suited for everyone, neither for every time period in our lives. If you still want to spend some quality time with yourself, find a reasonable solution that acknowledges and respects your time constraints.

As Theodore Roosevelt once said, 'Do what you can, with what you have, where you are.'

10. Do you think waking up at 5 a.m. is suitable for everyone? I know a lot of people who can't wake up before 9 a.m. and are still extremely productive. So why should I wake up at 5 a.m.? Why don't you create a personalized sleep schedule for everyone?

It's true. There are people who need less sleep; however, they represent the exception and not the rule. And for those who feel they need more sleep, this is due to decreased quality of sleep rather than quantity.

Based on my studies and practice as well as the practice of the 5 a.m. Club members, the essential hours for physical recovery are between 10 p.m. and 3 a.m., because during these hours you have the best chance of sleeping deeply, and this allows your body to consolidate its memory and unfold the other restorative processes.

At 9.30 p.m., melatonin is released into your body. To be more specific, it's your body's way of telling you it's time to get ready for bed. However, through the consumption of coffee, carbohydrates and sugar in the evening we manage to disrupt this process.

I recommend waking up at 5 a.m. for health reasons. Beyond these reasons, however, I fiercely believe that we need to put ourselves first, we need to load up on energy, confidence, significance and clarity before we begin our day so that we can achieve the best results possible and the highest level of productivity.

More important than waking up at 5 a.m., however, is the practice of starting your day by allotting quality time for yourself. Can you allot the first hour of the day to yourself? Or do you put yourself last, late at night when you're tired and burdened by problems?

11. Why is it that sometimes you wake up feeling very tired, feeling your body heavy even though you've slept for over eight hours? Even more so, there have been instances where I've woken up at 5 a.m., chose to stay in bed longer even though I felt rested and after sleeping two more hours and waking up at 7 a.m. I felt 'hung-over', tired and my body felt heavy.

There aren't compelling studies that reveal the exact negative side effects that sleeping more than eight hours per night has on a person's health. But this sleep behaviour has been correlated with depression and with difficulties regarding self-perception and the results achieved while performing day-to-day activities.

When you sleep longer than you should, even if you feel rested, then you're using sleep not as a means for recovery but as a replacement for your lack of willpower, an interest that ignites your passion for life or your disappointment towards yourself and your life.

It could also be the case that you woke up in the middle of a 90-minute sleep cycle during which time your body was filled with the analgesics that bring about sleep.

It really helps if you 'tell' your body that you're planning to wake up at X hour so that it may prepare for this situation.

12. Once I get to a point where I have been waking up at 5 a.m. for some time, is there a possibility that I don't want to wake up this early in the morning because I'll think I can do something else during the evening/day?

Implementing the habit of waking up at 5 a.m. is only possible when your WHY is strong enough and when you've already made a strong decision to move in this direction.

And this is only possible when your personal values are leading you in this direction. As you evolve and develop and as you change, your values change as well and it's normal for you to want something else, to set other goals. It's quite natural for your past decisions not to apply to the present circumstances.

But what I certainly can tell you is that the time you allot for yourself early in the morning will influence any objective you set. This time is of great help for your values because I'm convinced that everyone believes that they themselves are an important aspect of their life.

D. THE RITUALS OF 12 BUSY, BUT PRODUCTIVE, ENTREPRENEURS

ROBERT IGER
CEO, Disney

- Wake-up time: 4.30 a.m.
- He does some morning physical exercise (gymnastics at home or he goes to the gym).
- He has said that one of the few moments in which he feels completely relaxed is after he wakes up in the morning and does his physical exercises. Sometimes he does it in the dark, listening to music, especially to The Beatles.
- He reads speciality newspapers, answers his professional emails and watches TV, for professional purposes.
- Listens to music.
- Arrives at his office at about 6.30 a.m.
- In the first part of the day, he holds meetings with some of his key employees and uses this opportunity to motivate them and offer them honest feedback regarding their activities.
- He has a business lunch together with his collaborators.
- He spends at least two and a half hours daily revising details of the already opened Disney parks as well

as the ones that are due to open soon. He oversees everything from the setting up of the required spaces to the type of lighting and illumination used.

- He says he is available 24/7 for something related to the business he is leading.
- He is invited almost daily to have live television interviews from national networks such as USA Today, ESPN or ABC.

◆

HOWARD SCHULTZ

CEO, Starbucks

- Wake-up time: 4.30 a.m.
- He drinks coffee first thing in the morning, that he makes himself (remember, he is the CEO of Starbucks).
- Reads three specific newspapers on the topics that interest him (*The Seattle Times*, *The Wall Street Journal*, *The New York Times*). Has had this habit for over 20 years now.
- Rides his bike with his wife before going to work or walks the three dogs that he has.
- Listens to the messages recorded on his answering machine, which give him a wrap-up of the company's sales in the last 24 hours.
- Taking into account the fact that a new Starbucks franchise opens every five hours worldwide, Howard Schultz spends a big part of the day talking on the phone with his partners so that he can be updated as to how his business is going.
- Early in the morning, he talks with his partners in Europe. During the day, he keeps up-to-date with what is happening in the US. In the evening, he talks with his partners in Asia.
- He visits at least 25 Starbucks shops a week.

- He travels outside the country one week every two months. The time that he spends during flights is dedicated to reading.
- Howard follows a balanced diet. The ratio of carbohydrates, proteins and fats is 40:40:20.
- He practises at least 30 minutes of physical exercises six days per week (three days of cardio, three days on strength training).

◆

TIM COOK

CEO, Apple

- Wake-up time: 4.30 a.m.
- Answers his emails.
- He goes to the gym and eats healthy energy bars. He's passionate about physical activities, especially cycling, hiking and gymming.
- He's a workaholic. Every Sunday evening he holds video conferences together with his managers to prepare for the week to come.
- He's the first person to arrive at the office and the last one to leave. He works on holidays, including Christmas and New Year's Eve. He expects others to have the same attitude towards work.
- Tim Cook sometimes has lunch with his employees, which often turns out to be some sort of informal brainstorming session.
- A part of his time is dedicated to raising funds for those who suffer from multiple sclerosis, after he himself was mistakenly diagnosed with it in 1996.

◆

RICHARD BRANSON

CEO, Virgin

- Wake-up time: 5.45 a.m.
- He goes to the gym and then has a healthy breakfast.
- He has said that he cannot function without his to-do lists. He's constantly jotting down what he needs to do, checking off what has already been done. He reviews his lists regularly. He keeps it simple, using just paper and pen.
- The most important list that he makes is the one that includes the people he needs to call during the day. This list allows him to nurture his relationships and keep them at an optimal level.
- He has the habit of jotting down ideas that he has, comments and ideas from the people with whom he interacts, the names of his collaborators and the ways in which they can support him. He never throws out a notebook once it's full.
- He has the habit of facing his challenges before considering whether he is properly prepared. He takes time to plan, but he doesn't spend too much time on the details. He's more of a man of action.
- He's a fan of short breaks during the day, so he can recharge himself. Some of the things that help him to

relax are: a cup of English Breakfast tea, a hot bath, swimming in the ocean or playing tennis.

◆

ANTHONY ROBBINS

Author, speaker, entrepreneur

- Wake-up time: 5 a.m.
- He goes to the gym in the morning and drinks 0.5 litres of water.
- He reads inspirational books.
- He meditates.
- He practises visualizations.
- Each morning he allocates 15 minutes to self-care. During this time he does some physical exercise and breathing (for five minutes), then he does a gratitude practice (for five minutes) and, lastly, he does his affirmations (for five minutes).
- A part of his time is dedicated to planning. Short-term plans include his coaching sessions, business meetings, people he needs to call, interviews he needs to give, speeches and training.
- His long-term plans include meetings, international speeches, conferences and seminars.
- Every day he takes time to monitor the activities of his foundation, which is gathering funds for youth development, youth education through scholarships, rehabilitating ex-convicts and supporting the homeless.
- He allocates time every day to spend with his family,

even if he's away on international tours to promote his services as a speaker, a coach and a trainer.

- Every evening he revises his objectives list; he carefully checks the steps needed to achieve their fulfilment.
- Afterwards, he answers a series of questions which helps him realize what worked during that day and what he could do better the next day.

◆

OPRAH WINFREY

CEO, OWN

- Wake-up time: 5.45 a.m.
- She runs daily on the treadmill, followed by 45 minutes of cardio training, followed by 30 minutes of physical exercise to strengthen her muscles.
- She reads inspirational books.
- She writes in her gratitude journal.
- In terms of her dietary habits, she does not consume refined carbohydrates or any other source of amino acids.
- On an almost daily basis, she holds TV interviews or hosts live shows for national and international television networks.
- After lunch, Oprah carefully plans her next television projects.
- For daily relaxation, Oprah plays Scrabble against the computer for around 35-40 minutes on her iPad.
- She allocates time each day to take care of her soul project—Leadership Academy for Girls in South Africa.
- She has a light dinner and habitually does not eat three hours before going to bed.
- In the evening, she spends one hour reading books. She goes to bed before midnight.

ANDREA JUNG

CEO, Avon

- Wake-up time: 4 a.m.
- She goes to the gym for one hour.
- She arrives at her office at 8 a.m.
- When she comes back in the evening, she spends time reading books, surfing the Internet or researching information related to social media.
- She reviews her day in accordance with her to-do list that she has set for that day. She also writes down two to three activities that she wants to get done the next day.
- She jots down two to three events or actions that have made her feel proud during the day and at least one aspect that she should enhance the next day.
- In the evening, she spends one hour with her family and friends.
- Before going to bed, she disconnects from everything related to her business.
- She visualizes her success for the upcoming days and shuts off her mobile phone so that nobody disturbs her sleep.

◆

JEFF IMMELT

CEO, General Electric

- Wake-up time: 5.30 a.m.
- He does cardio exercises first thing in the morning.
- He reads the speciality press: *The Wall Street Journal* from the middle till the end, next he scans the FT Index and reads the second section of *The Financial Times*, next comes the business page of *The New York Times* and he throws the rest away. From *USA Today*, he reads the sports page, followed by the business page and ending with the Life section.
- He watches CNBC.
- He practises his affirmations.
- Over the course of a week, he works around 100 hours.
- Starting at 7 a.m., he meets with key investors in his company.
- After lunch, he holds presentations for potential clients of the company.
- During the day, he allocates special time to meet his employees (sometimes there are hundreds of them) so that he can present them with the company vision and receive feedback.
- Immelt takes care that his employees are aware of the news, business opportunities and the challenges the company is facing. To this end, he sends a weekly

email in which he offers such information. The email is translated into 12 languages so that each employee can understand it.

- At the end of his workday, he holds a meeting with his best sales people.
- Every evening he reviews his day and asks himself: 'What have I learned today? What can I do better tomorrow?'

◆

JEFF BEZOS

CEO, Amazon

- Wake-up time: 5 a.m.
- On a daily basis, he does his physical workout (he is preparing to be physically fit in order to go to space.)
- He has a healthy breakfast with his wife.
- He spends time on strategic planning for the next 10 years.
- Tuesdays and Thursdays are specifically reserved for productive work and on Mondays and Wednesdays he has meetings with his general managers.
- He surfs the Internet, especially e-commerce sites in order to find ideas and new perspectives that he could implement on Amazon.
- He cultivates the habit of saying 'thank you' to the people that have helped and supported him during the day, or for any other reason for that matter.
- He reads personal development and fiction books.
- He has the habit of carrying, at all times, a Moleskine notebook with him so that he can write down all the ideas that he has, no matter where he finds himself.
- He listens to podcasts and audiobooks whenever he is on the road.
- He practises visualization.

◆

ELON MUSK

CEO, Tesla, SpaceX and Solar City

- Wake-up time: 5.30 a.m.
- He runs in the morning and gets some fresh air.
- Next, he plans his day.
- He answers his professional emails.
- His work week is split between his two businesses: Mondays and Thursdays he is at his SpaceX offices and on Tuesdays and Wednesdays he is at the Tesla offices and Fridays are split between the two.
- Between 7.30 and 8 a.m. he heads to his office, depending on the day, to a different location.
- At 10 a.m. he talks on the phone with his vice presidents of different departments from the two companies, or holds interviews with journalists or job candidates.
- Between 11 and 12.30 p.m. he reviews and plans meetings with his engineers who design the rockets, in order to go over technical details.
- Between 1 and 2 p.m. he has a light lunch that he orders from nearby restaurants (e.g. chicken with vegetables and raw salad). During lunch, he talks with the people who are responsible for the various business facilities.
- Around 4.30 p.m. he goes for a walk around the

factory plants. He does this almost every day.

- At 7 p.m. he has a televised interview, followed by the premiere of the movie, for which he was the executive producer. In the evenings, he includes any other social activity.
- He reads personal development books.
- He answers his emails until late at night, even when he is spending time with his five small kids who are being supervised by a nanny.

◆

WARREN BUFFETT

CEO, Berkshire Hathaway

- Wake-up time: 6.45 a.m.
- He does light physical exercise, aerobics and muscle-toning exercises.
- He does not arrive at his office before the stock market opens.
- He has the habit of not scheduling his days, so that he can avoid meetings and wasting time.
- At work, he estimates that he spend 80 per cent of the time reading financial stats and data, stock journals and information about commodities.
- Later, he takes time to reflect upon what he has read and forms his own opinions and predictions.
- His recommendation to become smarter is to read at least 500 pages per day, sometimes he even gets to read 700–1,000 pages per day.
- He creates the discipline of not having a computer and a mobile on his desk while he is working.
- The remaining 20 per cent of the time he spends at the office, he gives short phone calls to his network, during which he has very concise and concrete questions regarding the companies he has been researching beforehand.
- He also writes letters to directly engage and connect

with companies that present a certain interest to him.

- He plays bridge 12 hours a week, sometimes against the computer and sometimes against his bridge partner, Bill Gates.
- He visits schools and high schools where he holds lectures on almost everything, using the Q&A method to get started.
- He lives in the same house that he bought in the fifties and eats at the same restaurants, usually a light and frugal menu.

◆

BILL GATES

Founder, Microsoft

- Wake-up time: 6 a.m.
- He drinks 0.5 litres of water upon waking up.
- He does his morning meditation.
- He reads the newspapers, *The Wall Street Journal*, *The New York Times* and *The Economist*, from the beginning till the end, and receives notifications with information about Berkshire Hathaway, where he is part of the Board of Directors.
- He drops his three children off at school.
- He makes his plans for the day and reviews the strategic planning he has for the next 10 years.
- Of the time spent outside of meetings at the office, two-thirds of his time is allocated to reading and answering emails. He has around 100 emails that he answers per day.
- A third of his work time is dedicated to Microsoft and two-thirds are dedicated to his charity foundation, which he manages with his wife.
- He reads books about subjects that interest him. He reads an average of five books per week.
- He goes to the gym.
- He picks up the kids from school.

- He has the habit of playing bridge whenever he find the time for it.
- In the evening, he does the dishes, even though there are others who could do them. He likes the way he does it.
- Before going to bed, he checks his email again.

E. THE 8-WEEK SYSTEM TEMPLATE (see the following page)

WEEK 1

8 min

	MON	TUE	WED	THU	FRI	SAT	SUN
Water 1 min							
Body Tough Love 2 min							
Breakfast 5 min							

WEEK 2 18 min	MON	TUE	WED	THU	FRI	SAT	SUN
Water 1 min							
Body Tough Love 2 min							
Shower 7 min							
Breakfast 10 min							

WEEK 3

21 min	MON	TUE	WED	THU	FRI	SAT	SUN
Water 2 min	☐	☐	☐	☐	☐	☐	☐
Body Tough Love 2 min	☐	☐	☐	☐	☐	☐	☐
Shower 10 min	☐	☐	☐	☐	☐	☐	☐
Breakfast 5 min	☐	☐	☐	☐	☐	☐	☐
One Question 3 min	☐	☐	☐	☐	☐	☐	☐

WEEK 4

28 min

	MON	TUE	WED	THU	FRI	SAT	SUN
Water 1 min							
Hawaiian Meditation 2 min							
Body Tough Love 2 min							
Shower 10 min							
Breakfast 5 min							
One Question 7 min							

WEEK 5

35 min

	MON	TUE	WED	THU	FRI	SAT	SUN
Water 1 min							
Hawaiian Meditation 7 min							
Body Tough Love 2 min							
Shower 10 min							
Breakfast 5 min							
Only One 7 min							
One Question 3 min							

WEEK 6 37 min	MON	TUE	WED	THU	FRI	SAT	SUN
Gratitude 2 min							
Water 1 min							
Hawaiian Meditation 7 min							
Body Tough Love 2 min							
Shower 10 min							
Breakfast 5 min							
Only One 7 min							
One Question 3 min							

WEEK 7

43 min	MON	TUE	WED	THU	FRI	SAT	SUN
Gratitude 2 min							
Water 1 min							
Hawaiian Meditation 7 min							
Body Tough Love 2 min							
Shower 10 min							
Breakfast 5 min							
Only One 7 min							
One Question 3 min							
12-Month Goals 6 min							

WEEK 8 47 min	MON	TUE	WED	THU	FRI	SAT	SUN
Gratitude 2 min							
Water 1 min							
Hawaiian Meditation 7 min							
Body Tough Love 2 min							
Shower 10 min							
Breakfast 5 min							
Only One 7 min							
One Question 3 min							
12-Month Goals 6 min							
Relationship Note 4 min							